Fun Returns

to

Great Toys

**A story about Steve, the CEO,
and his journey to rebuild a declining business.**

Book 2
The trials, challenges, and celebrations
of implementation.

By
Nick A. Shepherd

Jannas Publications

An EduVision Inc. Knowledge Service

Fun Returns to Great Toys

ISBN 978-1-7781309-1-5

Cover design by: EduVision Inc.
Jannas Publications

This is a work of fiction. All personal and company names, characters, business, events, and incidents are the products of the author's and other contributors imagination. Any resemblance to actual persons, living or dead, or actual events is purely coincidental. References to certain real organizations are meant for reader research purposes only. This book is set in the UK for convenience.

Dedication

To everyone who has affected my life's journey with your thoughts, opinions, ideas, criticism's, and other suggestions. Every event has been a learning experience and I thank you all.

To my family, especially my wife Janet and our children, their partners, and our grandchildren. You are the most important aspects of my life and in so many ways have contributed to my growth, learning and happiness.

To the army of people trying to make the world a better place for the future. It has been such a great experience to find kindred spirits in Canada, the UK, Australia, the USA and so many other countries, who are putting benefits to society above personal gain.

Steve's journey is a compendium of beliefs and life experiences. I especially dedicate these two books to Jim Bignal and his vision and mission of responsible business.

Contents

Our cast of characters

Alfred Eccles, founder Great Toys
Jack Eccles, Retired, son of Alfred.
Bob Eccles, Past CEO Great Toys, recently deceased
Francis Eccles, Bob's wife, board member Great Toys
Steve Eccles, CEO Great Toys
Jenny Eccles, Steve's wife.

Sarah Brightside, retired CEO of Fabrications Unlimited
Malcolm Brightside, son of Sarah
Heather Black, daughter of Sarah, owns her own marketing company

James Thackery, partner in accounting firm, Thackery &Thackery
Judy Dench, personal assistant to the Great Toys CEO
William Melnyk, owner / partner with Steve Eccles in a design business
Tony Jones, Director of Finance / CFO at Great Toys
Gord Mason, Director of Sales & Marketing, Great Toys.
Holly Rossi, Director of Human Resources, Great Toys
Charlene Johnstone, Director of Technical Development, Great Toys
Liz McIntyre, Director of Operations, Great Toys
John Jacobs, Marketing Manager, Great Toys
Mina Anwar, Team Leader, Culture Change Team, Great Toys
Janine Williams, Manager of the call center Great Toys
Josh Abrahams, Director of Sales, Great Toys
Julia Stevens, # 2 in Sales with educational experience (ECE)
Ned Bosher, ex employee (laid off) from Great Toys
Mark Peterson - Regional Manager, RBC (Bank)
Jean Lewinski - member of culture change team
Simon - member of Great Toys board
Brian - partner of Simon
Janet Parvane - part owner, facilitator Collective Minds
James Lee-Chin - new board member

Fun Returns to Great Toys

Fun Returns to Great Toys

1 Introduction

In book one, readers were introduced to Great Toys Ltd., a family owned business based in Two Rivers, England. The business was now in its third generation, after being started by Alfred Eccles in the 1920's. Alfred's son Jack, took over in the 1940's after returning from WW 2. Jack had two sons, Bob, and Steve, who both "grew up" in the business. After completing university, Bob started working for his father and was joined a few years later by his brother Steve.

The Great Toys brand had achieved cult status particularly amongst the "baby-boomers" generation. However, in the mid 1980's, the company was badly impacted by the "Transformer" revolution and the company's profits were hit. Being a family business, Great Toys were slow to make tough decisions about staffing levels. When they did, they also cut back on new product development. This challenge created growing internal conflict between Jack and his son Bob, and this was a major reason for Jack's decision to retire, although he remained Chairman of the board. At that point Bob became CEO.

As business became more difficult Steve and Bob also increasingly disagreed on the actions needed, and this, combined with the shortage of cash flow, resulted in Steve resigning, and moving to a nearby city where he went back to his initial passion of product design. Over the next ten years Bob continued to run Great Toys as CEO, while Steve successfully built his own company with his business partner William. Steve had little contact with the business, although he remained a shareholder.

All this changed when Bob's tenure was cut short in 2018 when he disappeared on a scuba-diving holiday in the Mediterranean. His wife reported him missing to the local authorities and some days later his body washed up on a small Greek island. His wife Francis and their two children returned home. After the funeral, the will was read and Bob's share in the business went to his wife. With no clear successor in the business, a new CEO was needed but Francis was unwilling to take on the role.

The board approached Steve Eccles as their choice as the next available family member to take over as CEO. When the call came, Steve had spent time checking out things with the family and others, and it had eventually been agreed that Steve would go back and give it a year at which point a permanent decision would be taken.

The first book "No Fun at Great Toys," starts soon after Steve's return to the business. What he finds, appears to him to be a dysfunctional and declining organization. Staff morale is low. Customers have been leaving. Suppliers are unhappy. Few new products have been developed and virtually none are in the pipeline. To make it worse, the bank is worried about the level of credit and is starting to ask about sale or liquidation.

Steve soon discovers that a number of these issues are symptoms of an increasingly competitive world, where Great Toys has tried to respond and sustain profits and viability, by focusing on restraint and cost cutting. By the time Steve arrived, this focus on sustaining financial performance has seriously depleted the ability of the Great Toys business model to recover. Steve needs to develop a different strategy. While making a profit and solving the financial issues remain imperative, Steve must also re-build the Great Toys business model. Core to this will be re-engaging the staff and building a more people-centric inclusive business.

Book one follows Steve's journey of discovery. Every day seems to bring new problems and issues. He has to balance the demands of the bank and investors, to keep them happy, while trying to understand the core issues, develop solutions and fix the underlying business. At one point someone suggests to him that this balance is like "doing heart surgery on a marathon runner, while they are still running."

Steve has the foundation of a good senior management team to build on, although he discovers that Gord Mason, the director of sales, who he thought was having performance problems, is burdened down with major family issues. As a result, Steve had to make some changes to his senior leadership team, appointing a new director of sales and upgrading another position to director of marketing.

When Steve initially returned as CEO, he was pleased to find there was a director of human resources, Holly Rossi. She has only been with Great Toys a short time and was brought in by Bob, mainly to focus on compliance issues, but it soon becomes clear that she shares many of Steve's concerns about the strategic approach to "people issues."

Book one has led us to the point where the basic problem analysis has been developed and a culture change team has been started, to gather information that will help Steve determine what is needed, where the key gaps and problems are and what changes are needed. Steve wants to build a foundation of "values based leadership."

One of the first actions Steve and his team have taken is to clarify organizational purpose, and to develop a statement around their commitment to the desired Great Toys business model. This has been supported by a "Stakeholder Values" document that has yet to be agreed and finalized. This will form the foundation of desired behaviours that are required to build a people-centric workplace.

Book two now takes us through into the implementation phase, led by Steve and his leadership team, supported by in-depth participation by the whole workforce of Great Toys. By the end of this book, they are well into the desired strategic shift but, as is summarized in the final chapters, these sorts of strategic shifts are a continuing journey.

Steve and his team already know there is more to do, as well as more opportunities to discover as they move forward. One key issue on Steve's mind will be determining the best way to embed these changes in Great Toys, so they truly form the culture and "the way we do things around here."

Just a warning – don't get frustrated! These two books reflect the reality of culture change within an organization. Many leaders fail in their efforts to achieve the desired turn-around because they lose patience and want it to happen fast. This reflects the challenge of both the business imperative to "get it done" but also the search for the "silver bullet solution." There isn't one. Changing behaviours takes time; every organization will be different but a window of at least three years is realistic, and that is what these books reflect – the first eighteen months of that process.

Typically, year one is understanding the problem; year two includes initial implementation together with learning what works and what needs further change. Year three will start to deliver results – more people will be on board; the metrics will start to reflect what management needs to know. This book is based on real scenarios from the authors personal experience. My first senior management role as part of a leadership team, was as a VP Finance; when we started we were a dysfunctional leadership group (one VP left the team shortly after). By the end of year three, our coaches and team development facilitators started to refer to our team as a "dynamo." It was now up to us. It was one of the best working experiences of my life. This "stuff" works!

2 Slow progress

"But it's just so frustrating" said Steve, "the Board is pressuring me to deliver results faster and the people in the company seem to think we can debate and talk about this forever."

Steve was having his weekly meeting with Sarah, who was acting as a mentor and coach. They had been working together for a number of months now. Sarah had sold her business but was still active locally and had met Steve when he returned to the family business to take over as CEO after his brother unexpectedly died.

"Remember I warned you about this Steve? We talked about people being your greatest asset but having a whole lot of other things that might drive you crazy. I could be flip and say, 'no pain - no gain' but I am sure you don't want to hear that."

Steve laughed. "I know, you're right."

Sarah continued "don't get me wrong, but you have to love people to make this sort of transition work. If you can't demonstrate that, you could face the danger of not being seen as authentic which is a critical leadership quality."

"I'm not sure I can love my employees - that seems far fetched. It might also lead to other problems if people started to think I loved them."

Now it was Sarah's turn to laugh. "Not individually Steve - but collectively. You have to love people collectively as an emotion - in the same way that you love chocolate or something else. You have to love their potential to excel and yet at the same time the emotional trauma that impacts their lives. Average people can do amazing things. You need to love human potential."

"OK I understand that but help me where you are going with this? I'm still frustrated." Steve shot back.

"Where I am headed Steve, is that you have to care deeply about those who come into contact with the business. Whether they are employees or contractors. Part time, temporary or contract. People at customers and suppliers. Unless, as a leader you can love 'the human condition' and demonstrate that you really do care about the workplace environment that you create, then it is going to be hard to be authentic and to survive the frustration of going through this culture building process."

"OK I think I see that" Steve replied. "Are you telling me this is part of the investment process in creating an effective culture?"

"Exactly" Sarah replied. "This process is costing you and your people time as well as the emotional investment. You are paying for this time - every minute, every hour, every day that you spend time developing the culture is an aspect of creating organizational value. It doesn't show on the financial balance sheet but, as I told you when we talked about the sale of my own business, the buyers put a value on the quality and effectiveness of our workplace. It not only enhances the way you operate it also builds the value of your investment."

"So that helps me understand the reason for hanging in there and going through this pain but are there any tips on how to make it more effective?" Steve asked. "Can I somehow shorten the timeframe?"

"Yes" Sarah responded, "but it's like a coach developing an athlete. Push too hard in too short a time and the quality of the results will deteriorate. It's about balance. I suggest that you are honest with the people on the Culture Change Team and tell them how you feel."

"Wow - share feelings. I thought business was about facts and 'the hard stuff.' Won't this show a weaker side of me? Surely leadership is about making decisions and setting direction and deploying your resources to get results?"

Again, Sarah laughed "good question and the answer is no, it won't weaken you. If done well, it will demonstrate that you have emotions just like the other team members. Great leadership is developing followers and that is an emotional relationship. What you want to demonstrate is inspiration and respect. You can get 'reluctant followers' who appear to do what you want but often if they are unengaged they will do it out of fear for you or fear for their job. Take the time to develop these relationships and the human dimension of the business will come out stronger."

"Before we finish Steve, how are things going with the Board? I know you are keeping them updated but have you had any feedback yet?"

Steve rolled his eyes. "Pretty much same as before. They seem to be happy with the short updates I give them but as I mentioned earlier I can tell they want results. It's a good thing that you and I are able to work together as I think that is reducing their concern. I have been giving some thought to the role of the board as we move forward. Do you have any advice?"

"Well since we are talking candidly, I think you might need to look at some changes at some point in the future. The board has been around a long time. On the one hand that is good - but as you saw last month when you presented your plans, your support is likely to come from people who understand what is happening in the real world. You need a mix of experience on the board - so you need some people with history but complemented by some who are - let's say, 'earlier in their careers.' The world is changing rapidly, and you need people providing guidance and oversight who are connected enough to support the decisions you need to make to implement change."

"Pretty much what I was thinking" Steve replied. "Can I ask you to just think about it and we can talk again later."

At that point Sarah looked at her watch and said she had to run and confirmed same time next week.

While Steve's agenda for change was a core strategic push he was also faced with the critical need to get some refreshed product out into the market place to demonstrate renewal of the product portfolio. He knew Charlene in product development was working with Liz in operations and John in marketing to move this forward. Charlene has sent Steve her regular weekly update report which seemed to show that everything was on track.

The new products would have to be in the catalogue in the next month, soon after which there was the toy trade show where samples would have to be available, so that sales could start pushing for orders for the next Christmas season. Having an increasing order board and backlog was a critical indicator that they would be able to stabilize their financial position and buy some time from the strategic shifts that were needed.

Steve gave Charlene a quick call asking how things were going and suggesting that they had a face-to-face update probably next week. This appeared to work out fine. Charlene also mentioned about progress.

"It is going to be tight Steve, as you know. Everything takes a bit longer than planned and there are always glitches, but we have a great team, and everyone is really committed. Interestingly in spite of the heavy work load I sense a level of excitement. It's as if we have a mission and we know we must succeed at all costs - so people are working well together. Occasionally things get a bit noisy, and emotions escalate, but everyone knows they are 'in it together' and we succeed or fail together - so that spirit allows us to get through the problems. Shared challenges seem to be important to building trust and cooperation as well as building friendships. So, long answer, its going well."

"That is great news Charlene, and I can't tell you how much I appreciate you picking this up and pushing it forward - but tell me, the hard bits. When are we going to have product available?"

"As you remember Steve we have four different initiatives. The first one was the 'quick fix" refurb of a few of the existing products. Liz is heading this up and we already have prototypes, so these will be first out of the gate."

"Super" Steve replied, "if I remember the second initiative was linking up with the local designers. How's that going?"

"I am personally looking after that one Steve and I can tell you it has been both challenging and stimulating at the same time. There are some amazing and creative people out there who just need the opportunity. My main challenge has been to instill a sense of urgency so we can move forward. There seems to be a personality trait with creative people that their work is not good enough yet and just needs a bit more modification. So, I have had to balance pushing yet supporting."

"That sounds familiar" – Steve laughed, thinking about his own work with the Culture Change Team. "Maybe you can give me some tips on how you did that?" Charlene replied that it was still very much a work-in-progress, but she would be sure to share her learnings.

"Anyway" she continued " we do have a number of new designs completed and in various stages of prototyping. So that part is underway. Liz has been leading the work with the supplier we chose to work with on the third initiative, using these new materials. We have also had Tony involved because there were some royalty agreements that we had to sort out - but again that is on track and will be the third set of new items to become available. I also know you had a meeting with their CEO as part of putting the agreement in place." Steve nodded in agreement, and Charlene continued.

"Finally, the customer driven ideas which was our fourth initiative. This has again been going quite well although the relationship re-building part of this has been a challenge. Anyway, even though these ideas are running a bit late we will be able to meet the deadlines."

"Perfect" Steve replied, "and thanks for the update. I don't want to slow your work done by more meetings, but do you have some get together's planned that I could sit in on just to get a bit more background?" They agreed that would work and the call ended.

One of the other major activities was the work of the Culture Change Team that Steve had been discussing with Holly. He was due to meet with them, so wanted to just check in with Holly, his director of HR, before he did that.

"Last time we talked, you had mentioned that as we move forward on developing and implementing the business model commitments and the stakeholder values, we would need to look at all our existing HR policies and procedures to make sure these are aligned and consistent. Have you done any more on this?" Steve asked.

"Two answers - Yes and No," Holly replied "Yes - I have looked at the challenge and I think it is going to be a bit bigger than maybe we realized, but before you ask, I have started working on an idea as to how we might do this. One key issue I have realized is that there must be a consistent and common message across all aspects of the HR framework, so the scope of the review is essentially everything. So 'No' I haven't moved ahead much further on this yet - in fact I am not planning on doing it until we have agreement on the final versions of both documents which are still in process with the Culture Change Team."

"I'm OK with that and it's a good segue into another thing. We are meeting with the team later - anything I need to know?"

"Not really. Progress is slower than we wanted and maybe we should try and get that point across. Other than that, I think their work is going well. From what I hear the sheer fact that we are asking for employees input and opinions is, in itself a bit of a motivator. This work combined with what they hear on the rumour mill about activity around new products seems to have lifted everyone's spirits up."

"Do you have any ideas about how I can push things along a bit faster" Steve asked.

Holly laughed "That, if I may say so is a typical CEO approach that has the potential to destroy things before we get started."

It was Steve's turn to laugh, although he was a bit concerned about the comment "Don't hold back Holly - I would be disappointed if I didn't get an honest answer - but on the other hand you know as well as I do that we have to make progress."

"Agreed Steve - but you have done a great job of allowing the flood gates to open. If at this stage we do anything that even suggests this is not a long term commitment to hearing the voice of the employee it can stop the process dead in its tracks. If you have concerns you need to express them; this is not about you exercising your power to make things happen but about being open about the reality of your own needs. Let's have the discussion but we need to make sure we don't leave the impression we want to take short cuts."

"OK - I hear you" Steve replied. "Can you make sure I stay on the straight and narrow then?"

Holly agreed and was about to leave when Steve said "just hold back a second. There is something else that is bothering me, and I need your advice."

"Fire away" Holly replied, wondering what new thoughts were now on Steve's mind. She was pleasantly surprised when he continued,

"You know we had some discussions about the social club and about the company having cut off funding. Didn't Ned also mention that when we saw him at the pub? Anyway, I have been thinking it over and it seems to me that we need a few quick wins to reinforce the message that we are serious about changing the way we do things around here."

"What do you have in mind" Holly asked.

"Could we have some sort of strategy to invest in the social club again? What I was thinking of is making the point that we are committed to doing this including starting with something small. Maybe we could then develop a phased approach where we gradually increase the funding as we improve our own financial position. I have spoken with Tony about the idea and although he cautioned me that we have very little discretionary money at the moment, he agrees with the idea as long as we start small. What do you think?"

"It's a great idea Steve and as you say it will reinforce the change we want to make. Let me work with the idea; there are still a few people that were involved originally in the club that I think would be happy to get reinvolved. I could bounce a few ideas around and see where they go. If it is OK with you, as I have been through this type of activity with other organizations, we need to combine our own responsibly for giving the support, with accountability from those running the club. I think we need to make sure that if we do re-start funding, the club develops a reasonable budget that matches what funding we can afford. Would that work as a way to get started?"

"Perfect" Steve replied. "Let me leave it to you. Can you also drop a note to the rest of the leadership team to let them know what is happening so that they are not blind-sided if they hear something?"

"Will do" Holly replied, and with that, they wrapped up the conversation.

THOUGHTS AND IDEAS

1. The process of engaging staff can be long and tedious and probably frustrate CEO's and others. Hang in there! It is an important investment in the business model.
2. Leadership is about caring enough to know what is important to people and helping them succeed. To lead effectively, you must love the people you are leading. Being a leader who leads with love, is to continuously develop your art of leadership.
3. Conflict should still exist in a great culture – but it is positive rather than negative. Focusing on issues not personalities.
4. As the changes move forward "alignment" especially with HR policies will be critical.

We will see Steve's role change from actively leading the change and being the change agent, to be one of guidance – developing as a coach, supporter, mentor, and facilitator. To embed a solid people-centric culture and build a responsible business, every employee must have time to discuss and buy-in.

3 Leaps of faith

It was not that Steve had been dreading the next meeting with the Culture Change team, but he certainly had reservations. If he was honest, it was about his own feelings. Steve remembered seeing another CEO of a large company talk about culture change and remembered the key points that he had made:

- Demonstrate (the change) by example.
- Be willing to sit down with others and share power.
- Be willing to give people the opportunity to make decisions on my behalf
- Give them the space and the power
- Focus on understanding that we all work together for a common purpose

Steve also remembered, because at the time it had hit him in terms of the personal impact, that the CEO had added

- I am incredibly outside my comfort zone
- I am giving up some of the levers of my own success
- It all starts partly with a leap of faith
- Current approaches to leadership are partly learned and partly as a result of an organizations culture.

These thoughts helped Steve, as he was obviously experiencing many similar reactions and reservations. He headed into the weekly Culture

Change Team meeting with a smile on his face and greeted everyone. They waited for a few stragglers to arrive and once they were all there, Mina Anwar the team leader, welcomes them all and set out the agenda which had been circulated before. They agreed the minutes of the last meeting and went to action items and follow up's.

The first item was to discuss the Purpose statement for Great Toys. This had been held up because the team had felt it would be a good approach - even though this was a little outside their mandate, to share the draft informally as part of their discussions on the business model and the values. This had been one of the issues for Steve but, wisely, he held back on making any comments at this point. Steve was surprised when Mina pulled a larger board from underneath the table and proudly stood it on the table.

OUR PURPOSE

To operate for the benefit of all our stakeholders, by creating trust and value while providing toys and experiences for education and entertainment

"We shared this with a lot of people in our culture change discussions and, while it did generate a lot of discussion, essentially everybody felt it was a good high level depiction of what we are trying to do. So, unless anybody has any additional comments, we are good to go with this Steve."

It went quiet for a short while and there seemed to be some apprehension in the room about his response.

"I am a bit taken aback" Steve said. "To be honest I think I was frightened that by giving more people the chance to look at this it would cause a perpetual process of wanting to change it and fine tune it. So, congratulations to you all. I am so happy that we now have one of our first milestones in place."

Smiles around the table and even a smattering of applause. "What do you think we should do next" Steve asked the team? Again, it appeared they were a bit surprised and asked what he meant.

"Well, we need to roll this out across the business so that we can truly point to a shared purpose - after all, this is what we are here to do."

There was some general discussion, and the conclusion was that to send the message of an engaged people culture, this should not be handed down "from on high" but should be rolled out jointly by managers and employees. The proposal was that the members of the culture change team would take the lead and would work with the head of each functional area to develop a plan that would allow for both communicating the statement but also discussing any issues and concerns. This was agreed and Steve took the action to work with his leadership team, so that they would support and participate in implementation.

The next agenda item was discussion of the statement related to the business model. This was seen as the bridge between the high level Purpose statement and the creation of a business model that would focus on the core stakeholders that needed to be developed, and how the company committed to working with each.

This document had been a bit of a challenge to the leadership team who had eventually agreed its content. They had been wanting to both reflect the key stakeholders such as all people, including employees, customers, suppliers, and investors but also to reflect their commitment to the larger society in particular the communities they operated in as well as the broader society. The latter part was particularly important given the need for business to address issues of climate change and social responsibility.

They had also had lengthy discussion about the larger "umbrella issue" of responsibility and accountability and had added an opening clause that stated their commitment to being "responsible stewards." They had agreed that this had broad application as many of the "assets" that were used in the business didn't belong to them and they had an implied trust from those providing these things.

Again, this was essentially good news. As Mina explained "we have made few changes Steve, based in input from our team meetings but I think at this stage we are agreed on this version." With that Mina showed the updated chart.

OUR BUSINESS MODEL

People are central to building the relationships we need for a sustainable business model that achieves our company Purpose. The desired outcomes include:

- ➢ *Ensuring a climate of responsible stewardship in everything we do*
- ➢ *Sustaining a safe and healthy workplace that nurtures and values all people*
- ➢ *Attracting investors through generating value and protecting capital.*
- ➢ *Serving customers needs with safe, value-based products and support*
- ➢ *Working with suppliers in a ___ mutually beneficial manner*
- ➢ *Providing continual improvement through knowledge, innovation, and creativity*
- ➢ *Ensuring zero harm to the natural environment*
- ➢ *Being a valued partner within society and the communities we operate in*

Mina continued, "you will notice a few changes Steve, and we all hope that you are OK with them. For many this might be seen as unnecessary 'word-smithing,' but we wanted to make sure that this commitment would be supported by the majority of staff.

"So, do those lines indicate where the changes are?" Steve asked, and Mina responded - "Exactly - let me run you through them," and with that Mina focused on each line:

- 'Ensuring' was originally 'creating.'
- 'Sustaining' was originally 'building.'
- In "working with suppliers.." we took out 'sustainable' as that is already in the heading
- We used 'improvement' instead of 'growth,' because the general opinion was that this was more relevant.
- We changed to 'ensuring' for the natural environment rather than 'working to achieve' as we felt that was a stronger commitment.
- We used 'being a valued partner' rather than 'Respecting and Contributing,' - again as we felt that this was more appropriate.

There were some added comments around the table and once again everyone waited for Steve's response.

"All seems well thought through and logical to me. I will take it back to the leadership team and see how they feel - but I think we may be good with this as well."

Mina replied, "that's great. So let me ask you Steve, and I hope I'm not putting you on the spot, but how are you feeling about the process so far?" Steve laughed and replied,

"Well, since we are making progress on how we feel about things, let me share some of my own feelings. First, let me congratulate you all on everything that you have done so far. I think we are making great progress; but my problem is that I am concerned about the amount of time this is taking. I really feel under pressure as a leader, uncomfortable even, that normally I would decide, and we would just go ahead. Now I have to wait and honestly it is frustrating."

Initially Steve was surprised when a few members of the Culture change Team chuckled and was almost ready to snap back "It's not a laughing matter you know." He was glad he didn't when Mina spoke up.

"It's interesting Steve because we share your frustration 100%. These discussions often take longer than we expect. Sometimes it takes time to get people to open up. Sometimes they can't make the meetings. Some time we run out of time because everybody wants to contribute. So yes, we understand. What we all need to figure out is how we can deal with it. We talked about it and right now we feel we are close to consensus on the "Values" statements, so we just want to have the time to close that effectively. In fact, we have told some of the people that discussion can't go on forever, but some of them have the concern that now they have a chance to have their say, it may not happen again. So, we need to think about that as well."

Steve smiled in relief. Sometimes the mistake managers make, is that they make assumptions on what can be done without knowing the reality of the issues involved. The reality is that in most cases, the people tasked with doing the job have exactly the same desire for urgency and closure. Wow - communications and assumptions again.

The team then went through the status of the "values" discussion around the group, and it was clear they were indeed near to closure; the team agreed that no more than two weeks would be needed to finish it up. This left them with the "next steps" discussion. It was already agreed that Steve would confirm agreement with the Purpose statement and the roll out approach so that was done. He could also now take the business model back to the leadership team and confirm that and it was agreed that assuming there were no issues, both the Purpose and the Business Model could be rolled out together.

The team wanted to wait until the Values were agreed before finalizing a roll out plan, but they felt that it should be similar to the others. It was agreed that there also needed to be a "cascading approach" so that every individual in a management and leadership position, would be both aware of the commitments but also "buy in" to the commitment. (After all, anyone in supervision, was in reality, the leader of one-on-one relationships in the organization. If behaviour was to change it must be constantly reinforced at that level). Holly was asked to give a quick summary of the plans ahead for changing many of the HR process to ensure they aligned with the business model and values commitments.

The team also wanted to discuss both their "learnings" from this discussion with employees but also tie this into how they would be able to sustain the values commitments going forward. as one said, "We have to move on from this being a project to where this approach to dialogue becomes part of the way we do things here."

Two ideas were floated but needed to be discussed later. First was the idea that "teams" was maybe the wrong term. Maybe "circles" or "groups" was more appropriate. This led to the second point that one of the key values from these discussions was obtaining opinions across different groups. There was a feeling that traditional functional "silos" often got in the way of collaboration and cooperation. So maybe the whole structure of organizing work needed to be changed. Having raised these as things to think about moving forward, the meeting broke up.

As they left the room Holly caught up with Steve to ask how he felt things were progressing.

"I'm glad you were there because it will help in taking this back to the leadership team. I was also appreciative of your warnings and suggestions before the meeting. I see now that sometimes it's better to let the conversation happen rather than jumping in with pre-determined assumptions. Thanks Holly."

Having spoken to Charlene earlier about progress on the new product launches, Steve wanted to check in with John Jacobs, his director of marketing, to ensure that both their social media development was progressing together with the marketing support for the new products. This was especially important as the next update with the bank was coming up and he wanted to be able to provide positive information.

"As they say, some good, some not so good" John replied, when Steve asked him for an update." Let me give you the good news first. We are well on the way with the integrated company social media plan, and already have one of my team posting about the company on a regular basis. He has set up company pages on a number of sites and already we are seeing a good growth in followers."

"So, are we on track with the rest of the social media launch?" Steve asked.

"Yes, it's going well, and we are on schedule. We have been working with Heather Black - Sarah's daughter, for some ideas in this area and she is emerging as a valuable resource. She has also taken a look at the web site, which as you know we had to do some quick fixes on, and she wants to also build in a re-vamp of the site so that it ties in with the whole branding focus through other channels."

"OK - what else?" Steve asked. "How about the new product launches?"

"The launch development for the new products is going well, although there is one glitch that I will come back to, but the other bit of good news is that Julia Stevens - remember she is Josh's number two in sales, has organized our first educational video on You Tube. I can e-mail you the URL so you can take a look. It seems to have been well received and actually links in with the launch of the upgraded versions of our current toys that Charlene has been working on."

"That sounds great" Steve replied - "but the glitch?"

"Nothing major" John responded. "I am having some budget issues with developing the sales support materials, as our funding had been cut back. I talked with Tony, and he is working to try and shuffle some money around so we can solve the problem. It's going to involve removing some money from somewhere else, so he may be chatting to you about it. I am being as prudent as I can but with the pre-Christmas catalogue, showroom and pre-ordering coming up we need to have enough of a presence to catch peoples eyes."

"Good Lord" Steve said. "I forget that we are close to needing product already - I know we have the sales targets, but it seems to have crept up on us."

"Not really" John replied. "Pre Christmas ordering takes place around April for deliveries in the summer and early fall; but no worries - we are working to a schedule to meet those dates and are on track. Everyone is working hard to make it happen."

They talked around a few more points and finished the discussion. Steve had set aside the evening to attend a local fund-raising being organized by the group that Sarah was involved with, that had renovated the local warehouses in the centre of town by the canal. A number of smaller, innovative companies now had their offices in this area, including Heather, who was helping John's marketing work. The fundraising group was also involved in a local venture capital fund that supported several of these organizations. Sarah had felt that it would be a good opportunity for Steve to get to know some of the other local business people.

It was an informal affair and so Steve headed directly there from work. As he walked in Sarah was already there and came to meet him. The first person she introduced Steve to, was Heather. They quickly started to reminisce about having grown up together in town, and soon they were deep in conversation. Sarah came back and a few minutes later reached out and pulled someone else into the conversation and introduced him to Steve.

"This is Paul - he is retired now but is involved with our little ventures here in town. Paul used to be involved in M&A's."

"Good to meet you" Steve replied. "Sounds like an interesting career in M&A. Any particular area?"

"I worked in the mid-sized range of organizations across a range of industries. Most of the work I did was for family businesses; either no one wanted to take over the business or in some cases for situations where the only options for expansion, or even to maintain critical mass was to merge. I also a did a few fire sales where business had been run down and again the investors wanted to get whatever money was left out of the organization."

"You must have seen a lot of things over the years. Anything stand out in particular?" Steve asked.

"Well part of the reason I was retired was things were changing. Organizations were getting harder to value and areas like culture were becoming more important is allowing a business to remain competitive. Honesty I became tired of trying to put good deals together only to see the buyer do things that focused only on the bottom line which often resulted in destroying the competitive advantage and seeing key people leave."

"Surely there were clauses in the agreements so that the buyers retained key staff?" Steve asked.

"Well, yes there were. Things like short term contracts and non-disclosure agreements and non-compete clauses. Lots of paperwork. But in many cases the ultimate call was being made by the new bosses, so people who stayed were often forced to take actions that they disagreed with. That left a lot of what we called the 'walking wounded.' People who were working out their contracts but really had no passion left in them. In many cases people just hung in until retirement rolled around. I know many of them tried to put on a good face, but people knew. If the leadership isn't clearly engaged and committed then you can be sure the rest of the organization won't be."

"That's really interesting" Steve replied.

"And let me tell you Steve, that's why a lot of us here in town are rooting for you as CEO of Great Toys. I think most of us felt it wouldn't be an easy transition, but from what we hear you are doing a great job. We are glad you are back in town."

Steve laughed "Well I must admit it is a challenge but on the other hand it has developed into a bit of a passion. As you know our family started the business and have been part of the community for a long time and I really believe as the owners we have a responsibility to run an effective and responsible business. You probably know that Sarah has been helping me and that has been very valuable."

"Taking of help" Paul replied, "we would all be happy to help in whatever way we can - but I have to tell you we have an ulterior motive."

"What would that be?" Steve asked.

"Well first, there are a lot of people living here whose families can trace their own history as part of the success of the Eccles family business. We think it is important to the community that the organizations who helped build the community remain as a key part of it. Eccles is at the core of a lot of people's lives Steve, and that is part of running a responsible business."

"I agree with that" Steve replied, "but some on, there must be another motive?"

Now it was Paul's turn to laugh. "Yes indeed. We want your time and your money. Let me explain before you tell me you don't have any money. We all know things take time to turn around, but your experience will be invaluable to other organizations in the community. Once you have things a bit sorted out, we want you to think about joining our Responsible Business initiative in the community, and help continue to support and develop local business."

"Where does the money come in" Steve asked, smiling.

"We know from Heather here that you are already working with several of the local designers in town and giving them a chance to grow their business in partnership with Great Toys." Steve nodded and Paul continued.

"We all think there is major opportunity to build more business by helping each other. This work you are doing is a great initiative and we would like to help support whatever you can do to expand this. As you may know we have a local venture capital fund that invests in some of these smaller starts-up's and your support provides additional help and leverage to them. So, we want to see you doing more of this - but down the road we also want to see you become a key part of this initiative. That why we want your money."

They both laughed, at which point Sarah returned and Steve and Paul parted ways. Sarah introduced Steve to several other people, many of whom it appeared already knew of the work that Steve was doing at Great Toys. In small towns word travels fast.

THOUGHTS AND IDEAS

1. For a leader "letting go" and "empowering people" can be very unsettling. Often leaders want to be "in control" – especially in terms of problems.
2. Better decisions will be made when those implementing them (most employees) have a role in suggesting approaches.
3. A leaders "leap of faith" in stepping back, is often repaid with a realization that most people want the same things.
4. Employees usually realize when things are taking longer than they should and if "empowered" will take responsibility for solving the problem.
5. No change process will be smooth. Even the process itself may throw up new problems(e.g., budget issues).
6. Leaders and everyone else constantly need to have the goals in mind to ensure the process delivers results.
7. Steve's initial "foray" into community involvement using a social event is a great way to start.

Effective leaders must break their own thinking, that only they know what needs to be done. The people at "the front lines" of the business see the problems everyday and are possibly even better at seeing operational solutions. The leader guides his whole business towards strategic goals while the actions to move progress forward MUST be delegated to the lowest level possible. The expression "wind them up and let them go" comes to mind – ensuring that purpose and values (the what and the how) are clear to everyone involved.

Fun Returns to Great Toys

4 Changes on multiple fronts

Steve had once again returned home to Jenny and the children for the weekend. One of the key topics for family discussion had continued to be what the family would do now that Steve had made the decision to continue on as CEO. A few weeks ago, he had raised the issue with the family because he was concerned about the integrity of making all these changes at Great Toys without people there knowing whether he would remain in the job once his twelve months were up. He was also getting tired of spending so much time away from the family and felt they needed to decide what they would all do.

While some people talked about managing the "work life balance" Steve felt that work was a part of your life, so it wasn't so much about balance as about making sure you liked what you were doing. Once he made the decision to stay, he had talked with the Board members, and they were happy he wanted to continue and so the decision had been made and announced internally. From the feedback he had received, his decision had been met with yet a further sign of optimism for the future. (Once again confirming the importance of leading by example - people do notice the personal decisions you make).

The family had agreed that there was no rush to move forward. The end of the school year was not for a few months, and at that point their eldest would be moving away to university anyway, leaving the other one completing their final year (at 6th form or high school). Jenny still had her career and if they moved, that would possibly require her to find another job - but with two careers involved, they both agreed they had equal weight in the decision making. At the moment the feeling was that they would keep the house and would continue to rent a property in Two Rivers, where the Great Toys was located, for at least a year until school was over.

Steve was mulling over things as he drove back to Two Rivers on Monday morning, having decided to stay at home on Sunday evening and make an early start. The drive was always more pleasant before the rush hour. Although he had a lot on his plate he was feeling energized by the changes being made and the progress. He wasn't sure they had all the "right people on the bus" yet but knew that issue would take a while to resolve.

Steve's main goal this week was to move towards agreement on the "values" so that everything else that rested on those behavioural statements could start moving ahead. He knew that the culture change team were planning on completing their initial work and wondered whether it would make more sense for them to do their feedback presentation with the whole leadership team - that would allow a complete discussion rather than Steve sort of acting like a go-between. He thought back to the issue of "letting go" and "giving people space and power to act." Maybe this would get the message across, but weren't the "discussions and actions of management" undertaken separately from the employees? Wouldn't this be taking transparency too far? He was in the "leap of faith" arena at this point - but if he did bring them all together, this would clearly illustrate the importance of the whole team approach.

Steve continued to think about this as he arrived at the office. He knew he had a meeting with Holly this morning so maybe he could get her thoughts. His first meeting was with Tony to discuss the current financial projections and the report to the bank; this was also the week for completing the quarterly report to the board.

"What are the numbers looking like?" Steve asked Tony, as they sat down.

"Challenging" Tony replied. "The good thing is that the marketing people are feeling very good about the potential for the new toys that are due to be launched; they have been working closely with sales and at the moment their projections after talking with clients are holding up - in fact a bit ahead of where we were last time we discussed it."

"So, if there is a good thing as you say, is there a bad thing to go with it?" Steve asked, obviously concerned. Keeping the bank and the board happy was a critical foundation for being able to move ahead with the strategic issues they were working on.

"Not really a problem. The challenge is that with all the activities we are working on, keeping a handle on expenses is hard - especially when you keep asking people to come and see me to find money for little extras and things we had not planned."

"Honestly Tony, the reason I do that is that I have the confidence in you to look after things and keep me out of trouble. I know we have some level of leeway in the budgets, and I think we both agree that our budgets, plans and projections should be guidance? I don't want us to get too rigid about 'whose pot of money' we are dealing with."

"While I agree with you" replied Tony, "you need to know that when it comes to spending, the culture here among the senior managers and several levels down into the organization, is that once budgets are agreed, managers feel they own the money. There are clearly cases where I know that people are going to underspend their expense plans, but they are very protective of the money. I often have somewhat heated arguments with some managers whenever I can clearly see an underspend trend and want to reallocate funding."

"But surely that goes against what we are trying to do as a leadership team? Are we running this business together as a system or are we running a bunch of fiefdoms, where everybody focuses on their own area?"

"I think maybe you know the answer to that" replied Tony. "While it has always been an issue because of the nature of functional budgets and silos, it was made worse after the continued cost cuts. Everybody protects their own money."

"So once again good old culture has to start at the top" replied Steve. "Does this mean we need to work on the "team-ness" of our leadership group as well as what we are doing elsewhere in the organizations? If the senior managers can't 'share and play well together' what hope is there lower down."

"My point exactly - so yes. We will need to work on this. I have been looking at our total budget as just that. Total budget. If the reality of our situation changes - which it clearly has, then we shuffle money from where it is to where we need it. So back to my point. This is the approach that I have been taking to make sure we can meet the projections, but it's fair to warn you that there may be some blow back from some managers."

"Good to know on both counts Tony. OK let's go with the projections as you have them. Work with Judy to get the summaries out to the board members for the meeting that is coming up and then you and I can meet with the bank."

With that they parted company. Steve was left thinking once again that while everything looked good on the surface - everyone supporting the changes in culture and encouraging cooperation, the reality was still a bit different. More work to do with the leadership team.

Steve knew that the board meeting was coming up, but he continued to be concerned about the - dare he think it, "quality" of the board. There were two issues bothering him. Firstly, the fact that he was still personally holding the position of Chairperson. While this was the norm for many organizations, Steve felt that effective governance required a board led by

"In a way it's the same old problem - micro-aggression. In spite of the positive responses that we are getting from the culture change work, I am still hearing issues about staff being upset by the way they are spoken to. Some have suggested that one of the things we need to introduce is a whistle-blower program, but I am not sure that makes sense."

"Not that I disagree with you, but what do you have against whistle-blower programs? Steve asked.

"In my experience" Holly responded, "they are usually a one size fits all type of system and the reality is that we have issues that range from small to large. Just to clarify, when I say large, that would be someone committing fraud whereas small would be issues like this. Issues where people who feel aggrieved just need an outlet."

"Like an escalation approach?" Steve asked.

"Well not really although that might be part of it." Holly replied. "I think we need a different process like a peer based arbitration approach. Maybe if that didn't work, there could be an escalation."

"I agree" Steve replied. "I certainly believe we do need some sort of safety valve system for people to raise issues. But let's not get off track - is there something we need to do now?"

"I have been thinking that we need a different type of awareness program. You and I both know that our typical diversity awareness programs don't necessarily change behaviour - in fact many attendees think its' a big joke. They don't get what the problem is in how they behave - so they take the course, but nothing changes. What I am thinking about is having some of our own minorities internally, actually work with me to develop and facilitate a program. We would concentrate less on legal issues and much more on one-on-one personal behaviour using role plays and real life experiences that they have been through in our own company. What do you think?"

Steve didn't hesitate "I think it's a really great idea. It should make it much more real. The danger may be that people get defensive or emotional when they are 'put on the spot;' maybe you should also think about an external facilitator who can be independent and objective to actually oversee each session? I'll leave that thought with you. Take a look at it. My suggestion would be that we defer starting for a few weeks so we can tie the whole thing back to our values."

"That's perfect" Holly replied. "Now to the other things. Just to let you know I have looked at what I think we will need to do and as I mentioned before it will be a major project and take some time. My goal is to develop an HR framework that is, for want of a better word, integrated. This - let's call it our IHRMS (Integrated HR Management System), would ensure that everything ties together. Values that we talk about are embedded everywhere. As part of hiring, orientation, leadership training, promotional plans, performance reviews. Everything - it all has to tie together and be complementary."

"That seems logical" Steve agreed, "but I notice you haven't talked about compensation?" Is that part of your approach?

"Absolutely" Holly replied. "Comp is a major issue; first I suggest we need to make sure that all of our approaches reflect as a minimum, market rates. But we also need to decide strategically where we want to be relative to market. We also need to link progression in pay to development and performance. It also needs to be transparent. There has been a policy here for some time now, that anything to do with pay is secret - and when that happens people talk, guess, make assumptions - and are usually wrong. But it raises dissent. I also think we need to think about our starting pay and minimum wage. I think if we are to align with our values we need to think about a *minimum living wage* and not just minimum wage as legislated. We know the two are different. Minimum range is usually not adequate to live on and leaves you just above poverty level. And not to put too much challenge to the subject, we also need to think about supplementary compensation such as incentive plans for sales, performance bonuses and our thoughts about profit sharing."

"I get the message" Steve replied. "This is going to be a challenge. What are you thinking in terms of plans, approach, and timing?"

"There is no way we can do all of this at once. My approach is start with getting the basic rates right and implementing fair starting salaries including the living wage. We then need to look at resolving any existing discrepancies that gives us. Then we need to work on the rest of the framework. I think at some point we should tell everybody where we are headed so at least they know changes are being made."

"OK - let's make that the plan." Steve replied. "You will need to run with this and keep the team updated on where we are headed. Now we also need to talk about the work of the culture change team. As you know we are due to hear their final input this week, but I am a bit concerned about how we approach correlating and integrating what they provide with the work we have done at the leadership team level. How do we make 'top down and bottom up' meet in the middle with something we can use?"

Holly thought for a few moments "we did give them a copy of what we created" she replied, "so they actually have both bits. If I remember what you asked them to provide feedback about was things such as:

- what employees generally believe would be a great workplace?
- What sort of behaviour would we be seeing?
- What behaviour would be unacceptable?
- What aspects would make up such a great workplace that people wanted to be here and contribute to their maximum potential? What would that look like."

Steve nodded and Holly continued, "So, I think that is the type of data the culture change team have gathered. We should ask them to come up with something based on what we created and tell us where they see problems - and possibly suggest some changes?"

Steve responded, "but then if I have to take that back to the leadership team, won't that just create more back and forward? What about if we ask them to present their findings directly to the leadership team. Do you think that would work or would they be intimidated?"

"If I remember" Holly replied, "you also suggested that 'once you have that information, then I would like you to tell us as management where the gaps are. What are the biggest things that need fixing and that can include actions that employees may suggest?' Was that correct?"

"Yes - that was the second part of their work," Steve confirmed.

Holly continued "then I think we need to trust the team to tell us what we need to hear as well as use this as an opportunity to show that management really wants to listen with an open mind."

"That might be a big risk" Steve replied, "for all of us. I can see people getting defensive and at worst delivering a message that this has all been a waste of time. Then where will we be?"

"Let me play it back though Steve. If we can make it work successfully, what a great message that will deliver. Remember there is no progress without risk. If we are serious about a change in behaviour it needs to start at the top."

"I can't disagree Holly but is there something we could do to at least mitigate the risk. Should we minimize discussion and just hear them out?"

"That would also be a problem. Honestly there is nothing worse than presenting to a 'stone wall' and having no idea what the audience is hearing. People will start watching body language and probably jump to all the wrong conclusions. No, if we are going to be serious we need to start opening things up. That's what we are as leaders after all. There is one thing I can suggest though that I think would definitely help; could we get help from a third party facilitator who can be impartial and mediate the discussions? At least that would reduce the risk of people being seen to take sides in the debate."

"That is a great idea" Steve replied. "Its short notice - any ideas?"

"I think the first person you want to talk to is Sarah. She certainly knows what you are trying to do and has been through this herself in her own company. Even if she is unavailable I am sure she knows someone who can do it."

"Great. I really appreciate your thoughts and inputs on this Holly. I will see what Sarah thinks and maybe we can do this as soon as the leadership meeting this week."

With that they parted company. Steve was finding it helpful to confide in Holly and she seemed more than a traditional HR person; she could think through people strategies from a business perspective and seemed to have a good feeling for the "feelings" side of things. In a way it was kind of like dealing with Tony in Finance - he knew the financial side of the business but was able to contribute this in the context of what was good for the business as a whole. He hoped that he could work with his whole team on this basis as his plans moved forward.

Steve called Sarah on her mobile and explained the background to the meeting. She already knew of the work on developing the values and after asking a few questions about Steve's concerns for the joint meeting, agreed to facilitate.

THOUGHTS AND IDEAS

1. Poor collaboration starts "at the top." If the leadership team fails to function as a cohesive group, it will not happen below.
2. The CEO and Director of Finance must work as partners. Resources including cash must be constantly assigned and re-assigned based on changing situations.
3. Traditional budgets are too rigid for competitive flexibility.
4. Steve knows he needs governance guidance at board level, and feels changes are needed. He takes the initiative.
5. Peoples behaviour will not change "overnight." Many will need coaching and support. Some may eventually not fit.
6. The whole "people framework" will need to be aligned. So many aspects impact how people believe they are treated and need to be aligned with the values.
7. Unfiltered feedback is crucial for effective management and leadership. This will require "attitude changes" at management level and an underlying "safety valve" system.

Culture is everything. Steve is discovering that effective implementation means development of his leadership team in parallel with changes across the organization. Leadership creates the climate where "the truth can be told." Independent, impartial, and experienced 3rd party facilitators are often needed to handle conflicts that will occur during development of both individuals and collective groups.

5 Reflections on the board

Steve had a few other activities before the Friday leadership team meeting although that was the key goal for the week. This week he also had his planned meeting with Simon about the board.

Once again he followed up with both Charlene and John on the new product initiatives. Everything remained on track and although there were financial challenges they both seemed to be working this out with Tony the finance director. They had also talked about the social media link to the new product launch which again was in place. John was falling a bit behind on the strategic approach to social media that would integrate the whole company branding with both products and services and with recruitment and their desire to increase community presence. Everybody was busy and this expansion of social media, was considered a lower priority than getting the revenues back up.

Tony and Steve had also had a follow up meeting with the bank which was a short affair. They had presented the updated financials and discussed the key strategic initiatives that were underway. Mark Peterson, the regional manager at the bank had attended the meeting and told them that their plans were very much aligned with what the bank had been hoping to see. He suggested to Steve that at some point they get together and see how the bank could help in any other way. However, Steve felt that with the workload, taking on new initiatives while important would need to be deferred.

The financials had also been sent to the board for their upcoming meeting. Steve was planning to both review the updated projections which showed his plans were moving ahead and on schedule. He was also hoping to be able to provide feedback on the Purpose, Business Model and Stakeholder Values at this coming meeting although the timeline was getting tight. At some point in the future Seve also felt that he would need to spend a longer session with the Board making sure that they had agreement on both these strategic statements they were making and how these were going to be operationally interpreted.

He didn't want to face Directors coming back and saying, "well that's not what I thought you meant when you said you were committing to XYZ." Steve didn't want to assume that he and the board were on the same page without investing some time in it - especially as many key decisions in areas such as capital expenditures would potentially be impacted by "values based decisions" versus being just financially focused.

One area that Steve knew he was going to have to address at some point was the link between peoples job satisfaction and ensuring that the company was providing them with the right tools and equipment. Steve knew personally that trying to avoid spending money on areas like state of the art / latest versions of software versus older versions - as well as older networks and hardware, often resulted in financial savings but lost productivity at the individual level.

Steve knew that there was nothing in financial reporting that showed the relationship between this and productivity - but he also knew from research provided by Gallup[i] that this was one of the most important issues on job satisfaction. (He had also read the book "First Break all the Rules" that demonstrated in great detail the most important questions to ask employees to assess satisfaction and he seemed to remember having the right tools and equipment was the number two question). Buried in their less than optimum productivity, partly caused by the culture was frustration caused by employees making do with equipment that they knew was slowing them down. If they were going to be successful in building the optimum culture, they would need to make sure they provided what employees needed. The challenge would be how to measure this and financially justify the ROI.

The time came for Steve's pub meeting with Simon; when he arrived, Simon was already there, and clearly knew several of the other people. They grabbed a table and Steve went to the bar to order the drinks. He returned to the table and Simon was looking at the menu.

"Anything look good tonight?" Steve asked.

Simon laughed replying "trust me Steve it's all good here. Have you eaten here before?"

"I am ashamed that my social visits are few and far between" Steve replied. "I knew this place was here by the river from when we grew up here. Doesn't seem like its changed much - although I remember if you wanted food you had to eat in the dining room in those days."

"Wow you are older than I thought" Simon said, laughing. "How many years were you actually away? I know a bit about the family background, but obviously I knew Bob better as he was the one who I worked with most on the board."

"It's over ten years" Steve replied, "and I don't know where the time went. A lot seems the same and yet a lot has changed. I hope you don't mind me asking but how did you joining the board come about?"

"Well, it was actually your dad when he was still alive and was Chair of the board. He apparently felt that some 'new blood' as he put it was needed and approached me. I had known him through shared business connections for a few years and he thought I could add some value - so here I am."

Steve then asked, "if I remember you retired some years ago but had your own IT business is that right?"

"Yes that's correct. I started the business as part of the high-tech boom, and it grew really quickly. We ended up being bought out by a global company and I stayed on for some time, but it was never the same. We lost the 'small company feel' that had been so important. As you may know IT people are considered by many to be a hard bunch to manage. They work strange hours and tend to be quite independent - yet they are usually incredibly creative. We were able to build a business around that, but when the company was sold many of our employees and contractors, felt they were 'institutionalized' and ended up somewhat demotivated. I stayed on for a while, but I am not sure that the new owners real 'got' the culture issue."

Steve smiled "now I begin to see why your seemed to be the one who understood what I was trying to deal with at the last board meeting."

"Oh, I get it Steve and I meant what I said. I think that you are on the right track - but I also realize it is a balancing act for you. Kind of like doing heart surgery on a marathon runner in the middle of a race. One slip and you kill the patient."

Again, they both laughed although Steve said he was not sure that he really liked the analogy of killing the patient. Only a figure of speech Simon had replied. They spent some time chatting and ordered something to eat. Simon had a quiche and salad and Steve decided to try the fish and chips. Once they had eaten, Steve returned to the main conversation.

"So, tell me , given that you came on the board as some new blood, how do you view things now?"

Simon thought about it and replied "it's been a challenge and I will be honest after your dad passed on there were a few times when I wondered whether I should stay on the board. The decisions were basically made in the interest of the family and Bob's tactics were focused on keeping earnings growing. In the latter years I was increasingly concerned but as a private company our advice was always just that - advice."

"Do you think that needs to change?" Steve asked, "in terms of how the board works? Obviously you know that I believe that we need to take a different direction, but should the board be more than oversight? Maybe I am afraid to ask the question, but I will. Should I, as the CEO just be able to do what I feel best?"

"I think any board, advisory or some other title, can add value if the CEO wants it to - so to that degree its up to you Steve, and the family I suppose."

"I think you can see from the last meeting I really do want advice Simon. As CEO, the final decisions are either mine or as a minimum the collective vote of the family shareholders. I guess if there are disagreements, family owners could decide to remove me, but I don't want to see us get to that position. If I want it to work as a truly advisory board with an objective and independent bias, what do we need to do?"

"If that is the direction you want to take, I think there are three issues you are going to have to address. First, you cannot stay on as Chair of the board - it must be someone independent and objective. As you know many modern governance requirements[ii] either mandate the separation of the CEO / Chair roles or as a minimum recommend separating it."

"OK" Steve replied, "that makes sense. What else?"

"You need some additional outside blood on the board with some more current experience. Business has changed. You know it and are trying to respond, but you need a board who understands and support change. You don't have the time to explain everything in detail. Yes, you have to be accountable, but to a board that understands the need for the changes - and I am not sure we have that at the moment."

"And your third point?" Steve asked.

"This is much more of a challenge, and I am not even sure how you might feel about it. I know you are committed to a much higher level of employee engagement. My belief is that moving forward organizations are going to have to structure their governance frameworks so that the 'voice of the employee' is being heard."

"Yes but is that an operational issue or an oversight and board issue" Steve asked?

"It's both - and in a private company, you can decide which route to go to achieve it. If you want an independent board that can truly support a people-centric strategy then that voice must be heard at the board level. As you may know the governance approaches in Germany and several other countries include a two tier board structure so that all stakeholders are given a say in corporate governance, not just shareholders."

"That is certainly the sort of direction I think we should go in. One open question for me is whether we should even think down the road, of opening the board up to ownership by employees. That could help with succession planning as well as broaden the investor base and give employees a more vested interest" Steve replied.

"My advice is put that idea on the back burner at the moment Steve - it is way to early to think about that before the whole business model is on a solid foundation; but I do personally think that its an idea worth pursuing."

"Fine. Say I agree with your three points Simon" Steve replied, " then how do we do this? I can't really suggest board changes and we don't have a board governance committee. Even if I agreed that we needed to do this, where would I start?"

"In my view the answer is simple. You wouldn't. I don't think this is best handled directly by you. You need to remain independent - in fact I think that the fact that you may want to relinquish your position as Chair kind of supports you not leading the charge. If you are OK with it, I would be happy to talk with my fellow board members and start the thought process. I will tell them that you approached me for advice - after all you remember one of the Directors even suggested at the last meeting that I should be the one to support you. If you are happy for me to do that, you can leave it in my hands."

"That's fantastic" Steve replied. "Are you sure you are OK with that - will it be alright with the other board members?"

"Honestly I think they will be relieved to hear that you are thinking about enhanced oversight Steve. Many boards have to force more oversight on their CEO' and here are you asking for more help and supervision. That's a great starting point."

"Agreed," Steve replied, reaching out to shake Simon's hand. As they shook hands Steve noticed a wedding ring on Simon's hand. "Oh, and I see you are married" Steve says.

"Well yes I am, Steve" Simon replies "happily married for several years now to my partner Brian."

"Oh" Steve replied.

Simon saw his reaction and laughed. "Well, it does come as a surprise to many people, but I have to tell you we have a great relationship."

Steve had recovered his composure somewhat and smiled. "I am sorry that I probably reacted like some people do Simon; I honestly can say I am so happy for you both. If anybody can find more love in the world today with another human being, that makes the world a better place for all of us."

Simon thanked Steve and told him some more about the history of his relationship with Brian and their families and how they had met. Then he added:

"While this may be premature Steve, I think that my personal situation gives me, how might you say, an inside view of areas like diversity and inclusion. As we move forward with your changes I would be happy to both represent those interests at the board level as well as support you at the operational level with developing truly inclusive approaches to human relationships - if that would work?"

"It would certainly work" Steve replied "and let's keep it in mind. Given that you are offering to do that, I have to ask do the other board members know your situation?"

Simon laughed, "yes they do. I shared it with them early on, as I felt it was an important thing for them to know. I think a few were surprised and caught off-guard, but we have a good working relationship."

After some more talk both decided it was time to leave. Both Steve and Simon had agreed it had been a very valuable discussion. Simon would start to think through and map out his approach and would keep Steve informed. A good evenings work Steve thought as he headed home.

THOUGHTS AND IDEAS

1. Steve is starting to realize that the information he has to run the business is also going to need broadening beyond finance.
2. Building relationships – for example with Simon, is critical to developing a network of trusted advisors.
3. Notice that Steve is constantly thinking about the various initiatives, so that he can keep up with what is happening.
4. Having a diverse board can significantly help guide the operational implementation and changing social expectations.
5. Real "inclusion and diversity" only arrives when there is no reaction to non-traditional relationships and backgrounds. Even Steve is still learning.

Steve is starting to act like the conductor of an orchestra. Working towards building his organization of leaders and other stakeholders that share a common purpose and system of values. His current role is to ensure the gradual development and building of an integrated and responsible business model.

Fun Returns to Great Toys

6 Agreeing the Values

By the time Friday came around Steve was increasingly worried about the leadership team meeting and the discussion around values. He had agreed to meet with Mina Anwar, the leader of the culture change team together with Sarah, who had agreed to facilitate the discussion. It was a good opportunity for the two of them to meet and share some thoughts and ideas. While Sarah was aware of the amount of work Mina and her team had undertaken, they had not actually met. Steve had kept Sarah up to date on the process, but this was to be the culmination of all the data gathering, which would lead to the foundation of a plan to both agree on the values, but more importantly identify the gaps and start an action plan.

Sarah felt she needed some background on all the people involved; although she had been working closely with Steve, Sarah had not yet worked directly with any of the leadership team, nor did she know any of the culture change team members. Steve had asked Judy to prepare a summary of all the attendees, with a short bio on each one as a briefing document for Sarah, and this was a key part of their pre-meeting discussion. Sarah had already read the materials but asked a number of questions about the attendees and their backgrounds and also their potential approach to these discussions. Sarah felt that to remain objective and keep things moving in the meeting, the more she was prepared the less surprises she would have.

They had almost completed their conversation and covered all the people on the list when they arrived at the name of Jean Lewinski, who was one of

Mina's team members. Jean had been with the company some time and by all accounts was a solid employee although there were some notes in her employee file related to prior disciplinary actions.

"What was all that about" Steve asked?

Mina smiled, "ah, Jean. Yes. Well, this is someone we need to spend a few moments on. Let me start by saying Jean is really committed to this effort we are involved in, but you need to know she comes with some background."

"As we all do" Sarah laughed. "What do we need to know?"

"My concern is that Jean might appear to be a bit of a skeptic" Mina continued, "and if the discussions turn heated she might say some things which seem to be aggressive and negative. But you have to know that a lot of it is because of a history of trying to make change happen in the company but running up against a brick wall."

"OK that's fine - it's good to have some passionate people involved but is there more? Sarah asked.

"Some years ago, when people were being laid off, Jean was active in trying to get a union into the company. Mina replied. "She signed up enough people for a vote but because of the family ties and the loyalty that still existed, when the vote was held there were not enough numbers. She had quite a run-in with her manager at the time, who was Liz - Jean was working in Operations. Bob got involved and was able to calm things down, but it left Jean with a feeling of unfairness in the way she was treated which is still below the surface."

"That good to know" Steve replied, "but you say she is positive and committed to this culture change initiative?"

"No question" Mina responded, "but people don't forget. It's like the story someone told me once about change. You can't come in as a new leader and tell everybody the rules are changing. Typically, people see you 'waving the white flag' for the want of a better expression, but they often say to the person next to them ' you stick your head out above the trench and if doesn't get blown off, I will start believing that things really will change. That's where we are today - people are supportive of the changes you seem to want to make; but its not the 90% that you do right that will convince them, it's the 10% you slip up on, where they will say - 'see, I knew you were not serious. So, we have to stay the course, weather the outburst and storms and build a track record of enough positives that the risk of negatives is reduced."

"So, you are suggesting I need to know about it, and if it happens manage it in a way that keeps the discussion positive?" Sarah asked.

"If we can do that we will be in good shape. Maybe there won't be a problem" Mina replied, "we will see." They continued and finalized the discussion and walked to the meeting room to join the others who were arriving for the sandwich lunch. Although these was some mixing it was clear that there were still two groups in the room. Change was obviously not going to happen overnight.

Once lunch was over Steve called the meeting to order and introduced Sarah; everybody was aware of her role but had not yet met her. Sarah talked a bit about her background and how she wanted to approach the discussions. She called for tolerance, openness, a willingness to listen and not judge, and to see disagreements as a basis for discussion not as final positions. Sarah had agreed with Steve prior to the meeting that the discussions needed to be reasonably open ended as setting an unreasonable time limit that ended up cutting off discussions would do more harm than good.

Sarah suggested that they approached the discussion in four parts. First the floor would be open to the culture change team who would present their findings. Then the whole group would go through the information and create a list of agree, agree with reservations, and disagree. This would lead to an open discussion on firstly "agree with reservations" and then on the disagree" items. The third step would be to compare the final outcomes with the "Stakeholder Values" chart and see if and how that needed to be modified to arrive at consensus. Finally - and Sarah suggested this may not even be achieved at this meeting, the gap analysis would be discussed to suggest where the most important changes needed to be made. Judy had been asked to keep notes and record information on the flip chart as it was discussed.

Findings of the Culture Change Team

The opening discussions were led by Mina on behalf of the team; to start, Mina introduced everybody and provided a recap of what they had been asked to do and explained the various approaches they had used such as some limited survey work, face-to-face meetings, focus groups, and an internal blog / bulletin board they had set up for open comments.

"When Steve and I first talked, he had asked us to try and discover what would make a great workplace. Somewhere people could be proud of that would attract and retain staff. Somewhere that people would look forward to coming to work (as you can imagine there were some comments and even some laughter of disbelief about this request.) Here are the key questions as a reminder:

- What do employees generally believe would represent a great workplace?
- What sort of behaviour would we be seeing in the workplace?
- What behaviour would be unacceptable?
- What aspects would make up such a great workplace that people wanted to be here and contribute to their maximum potential? What would that look like?

Mina continued, "because much of discussion we had, came from open ended input from staff at all levels, we as a team spent quite a bit of time working through it and came up with two lists. The first one is a selection of comments that people made about what would make a good workplace. We tried to develop things into themes, so in many cases we combined input that might have been worded a bit differently but represents, let's say variations on the theme." At that point Mina put up the first list.

Clarity. Where is the company going? What is my part and how do I fit in? How do we know how we are doing? How can I improve?

Supportive. People have the equipment for the work. Problems are resolved quickly. No blame - focus on solutions. Proper training and development. Opportunities for growth. Structured OJT. Caring. Trust. Fun.

Collaborative. Work together - cooperative, no silos. Share ideas. Everyone has a say no matter title / position. Realistic challenge. Build on strengths.

Fair. Open communication. Fair pay. Fair treatment. Shared rewards from success. Equal opportunity / no discrimination. Fair workload.

Honest. Minimum secrets. Ethical. Authentic leadership - tell the truth. Internal promotion where possible.

Safe. Concerned about people - physical, mental, well-being. Don't judge. No (unreasonable) surprises. Value diversity / inclusive.

Competent. Supervisors (leaders) who listen and know people. Required knowledge available / shared.

Mina ran through the items on the list, in some cases explaining and expanding what the input was, behind the information presented. She then explained that they had used this approach because people found it easier to think about situations where things had not been positive in the workplace. Then they could identify what a workplace would look like if those things didn't happen. She then explained that the team had used this list to develop a number of behavioural qualities that the team thought would support creating this type of workplace. Mina went to lengths to explain the challenge that the team had, in trying to "go behind" the words. As an example, she quoted that when they used a "caring workplace" the team had seen this as meaning many things from caring about the environment, to caring about the community as well as each other.

She also pointed out that there were overlaps between areas. What they had tried to do was end up with a list of qualities or values that problem situations could be evaluated against, to see whether the behaviour had been consistent. She finished by telling the group that the team had learned through this process, that most people really did care about a positive and productive workspace and most felt strongly that if management helped to jointly create this, everyone would not only be happier and healthier, but performance would almost certainly improve. She then put up the list of behaviours that the team had developed.

Trusting	Supportive	Positive
Open	Cooperative	Collaborative
Fun	Fair	Honest
Sharing	Challenging	Equality
Ethical	Caring	Authentic
Competent	Inclusive	Safe
Diverse	Accountable	Considerate
Responsible		Respectful

Mina let the group take a look at it and then Sarah asked if there were any questions. There was quite a lot of discussion but overall, it appeared that the list created from the culture change team was very similar to the items that the leadership team had developed.

This was a good time for a break and so they took ten minutes and re-grouped. Sarah had been working with Judy in the break, and they had compared the behaviours or values from the work that the leadership team did, with the list that the culture change team had put forward.

What can we agree on?

"It seems to me that we have agreement on almost half the list" said Sarah as she re-started the meeting. "We went through and compared the two lists - so can I suggest that those items can be accepted?" Everyone agreed that made sense. The following discussion resulted in a lot of "word-smithing" to either combine words or add and delete suggestions. Eventually the group was able to agree, amalgamate or delete certain items from the list.

The one major heated discussion arose when the group was trying to address "equality" and "authentic." The leadership team had already come up with "integrity" and felt that "authentic" was similar. The CCT strongly felt that from what they had heard from employees "authentic" was a bigger issue - that the failure of management to be authentic - that was the opinion of many people, they were suggesting that management often acted with a lack of integrity. That discussion became quite emotional, but Sarah was able to navigate their way through it. However, the emotions from this discussion finally boiled over during the talk about "equality."

The context of the CCT input was that "fairness," which had already been agreed as being on both teams lists, was similar to equality. Management felt strongly that using "fair or fairness" was enough. This was the point where Jean finally boiled over. Pointing at Steve she said:

"You just don't get it do you? In fact, I don't think you have any idea about what equity and equality really means from the workers point of view. You talk about us 'all being in this together' and how you need our support and help, but you are the one who gets all the benefits. We work our brains out to turn the business around which your family screwed up and our friends lost their jobs. Now you realize you need us, but who gets to benefit? You and the family. Your big salary, fancy car, and nice houses. There's no equality in compensation nor is it fair. If you want us to believe that things will change you need to tell us what is in it for us? That's equality."

Sarah tried to cool things down and moderate the discussion but unfortunately Liz ignored her and spoke over the top:

"Well, that's rich coming from you Jean. You tried to get a union in here when we were all going through hard times and Steve's brother was doing the best he could. You can't deny that was to protect your own interests was it? That's all we needed at that time was a difficult and unbending union getting in the way. Now you are at it again trying to suggest Steve isn't honest in what he's trying to do. He's trying to save your job. That's what you get out of it my friend. Your job. You should be thankful that he cares enough about you to bother. Maybe you should find something else to do."

Sarah had clearly heard enough and needed to settle things back down again. The challenge was if they took a break people with high emotions might make their escape. She needed to de-fuse the situation in the room so that everybody was part of the process.

"Let's take a second to stop our talk about values and look at what happened here. I know Liz and Jean are passionate about things, so let's give them both some time without judging. What did the rest of you see what happened here?" After a few moments Mina jumped in.

"I think it was a great exchange and probably one of most honest displays of emotion that we could have seen. Clearly Liz and Jean both care about the company and are here and want to be part of it."

"Charlene added "we also get to see that it is often easy to talk about facts and agree on things like openness and honesty and all the things we have just agreed upon, but when it comes to applying them in practice, sometimes our history and emotions get in the way."

"Great" Sarah replied. "Steve, you were just put in the firing line. How do you feel?"

"Hm," Steve replied. "How do I feel? Well, my first reaction was also emotional, although nobody heard me say anything, but I was a bit 'pissed off' to be honest. Maybe my body language could have given me away if anybody was watching. But I am glad I had time to reflect because a wise person told me to avoid escalation by not ***reacting*** especially when we feel the need to reply to defend ourselves. I think they said, 'to allow a gap between the senders message and the receivers response for thinking rather than reacting."

"OK" Sarah replied, "but after the gap what were your thoughts?"

"I realized that Jean was expressing what was her reality. Given that is the case, it's important to listen to what she is saying and try to understand what's behind it, rather than assuming her opinions are wrong. I think that Jean needs some unemotional space from us to talk about what the underlying problem is."

"So, Jean, on reflection what are your thoughts?" Sarah asked.

Clearly Jean had calmed down a little and paused before responding.

"I have always believed that beneath everything we are all the same" she said. "I sometimes get angry when I see what I consider to be things that are both unfair and inequitable because that builds barriers. It creates 'them and us.' In the past management and the workers were clearly not equal. Management used its' power to make decisions often without employee input, and often had no understanding of the reality of the work involved."

"Now that's fair" Steve replied. "I agree with you and that's what we need to change."

"But Steve you are only addressing part of the issue here. Jean replied. "Sure, we all want that barrier to come down and to be 'all in it together' but things remain that make us unequal. Maybe we can change some of these things by allowing workers to have a say and opinions to be listened to. But the elephant in the room as they talk about, is how to change our relationships from being unequal to be equal in terms of input to business decisions as well as dealing with fairness. Let me go back to my example - and tell me if I am wrong. The business as it is having problems right?"

"Agreed" Steve replied. "And I have to tell you that your comments about management being to blame is pretty close to the truth, although it hurts to admit it. Sometimes we have what could even be called a 'sacred trust of leadership' in our hands because its not just my money and the families money at risk. It's your lives, and those of your families that are at risk. Our suppliers and their people. Our community. Everybody who is part of our eco-system. So yes, we need to be better managers - and I think that starts with greater involvement of all the people."

"So, if you need our help in fixing the business, wouldn't it be more equitable if we had some benefit from the improvements, apart from, as Liz says, keeping our jobs?"

"I apologize Jean," Liz responded. "My comments were uncalled for. I know you want more than that and I understand."

"I appreciate that Liz," Jean replied, "it means a lot; but let's look at the equity issue. Steve, you may remember that when the team talked with you initially we talked about profit sharing. That was some of the reasons behind that request."

"But let's be honest Jean," Steve replied, "its' more than that isn't it. If we really want to build in 'the voice of the employee' to the business permanently we need to have some way of doing that as well?"

"Well, we hadn't necessarily got that far yet" Jean replied, "but I will defer to my colleagues - is being equitable more than just financial sharing?"

There was general agreement that the shift that was being looked for, was mainly a change to the way in which employees participated in the way the business was operated.

After some discussion Steve said, "Let's agree that is an issue we need to work on. We need to look at fair compensation, but we also need to focus on equitable returns and a sharing of performance improvements, but also some change in the way we manage the business, so that employee input is a much higher priority in decision making. This is in fact something I have been talking about, but we are in the early stages - but it is something I totally agree with, if we are going to perpetuate the cultural changes we are seeking."

"Are we done with the behavioural values then?" Sarah asked. There was agreement that everybody accepted that the current words that had been selected did reflect the combined view of both groups.

"Fantastic" Sarah replied. "Now we need to go to the next step and put these words into a statement that we can create, about what type of organization we want to be seen to be."

Matching Stakeholder expectations to behavioural ideas
After another short break the group re-convened, and a few questions were raised as to how much longer this was going to take. Clearly people were tired. It had been a long afternoon and for several people quite emotional.

Sarah, sensing the climate in the rooms, looked at Steve and suggested

"What if we start by looking at the statement that the leadership team already created? If we have achieved agreement with the words that we are using, and those words are already embedded in our "Stakeholder Values" do we need to do anything else? Can we just use that?"

Sarah asked Judy to put the statement up on the screen for everyone to look at.

OUR STAKEHOLDER VALUES

People are the heart of our Stakeholder community; they bring their skills and capabilities, work together, and build relationships through which we achieve our purpose. We believe in creating and sustaining a culture of engaged and committed people that:

- *Reflects passion, integrity, humility, and individual accountability, and responsibility.*
- *Builds people up through caring, respect, dignity, empathy, kindness, encouragement*
- *Is respectful, considerate, fair, ethical, inclusive, open, honest, kind, and encouraging.*
- *Embraces curiousness, effective communications, and engaged listening*
- *Is thoughtful, cooperative, collaborative, innovative, creative, and adaptable*
- *Creates a foundation for trust and a sustainable future*
- *Delivers results and adds value to each other and our community*

A member of Mina's team spoke up "It looks to me like this list has more words or values than we agreed upon. Do we want to just accept these additional words even if our team didn't come up with them originally?"

62

Steve replied "I don't want to over-ride anybody, but it would be great if we could do that. There are several words on there that are not really values anyway - there are things like "create value," "Results and sustainability" and some others, so its probably only a few words."

Sarah replied "I think its' up to Mina's team. They are the ones who were not involved in developing this - if I am correct?" Several people nodded. "Then I think its' their call."

There were a few visible signs of body language from members of the leadership team suggesting that they were done and should just move ahead with what management decided. Sarah noticed and as a good facilitator suggested:

"I know this is frustrating for several of you who just want to get going and get back to work, but we do need to, as was said earlier, 'do what we say we will do.' If Mina's team is uncomfortable, we need to give them their say."

"I agree" Steve added. "Look, it's late and we still have a lot to do. This is too important to cut corners at this point. Why don't we do this. Mina, can you arrange for your culture change team to look through this statement and see if you can live with it. I think we should assume that we will probably be adjusting it, as we roll it out anyway." Mina looked at her team who all agreed. Steve continued.

"We didn't get to the final part yet, which is the gap analysis. To me this is a critical action plan going forward and I don't want to rush it. Can we agree to pick it back up next week? Could we get together say mid-week so we can keep the momentum going?"

Everybody agreed and after some closing comments and wrap up, everybody thanked Sarah for facilitating and went on their way. Steve asked Sarah, Mina, and Holly if they could meet for a quick recap; they also asked Judy to join them with her notes from the meeting.

"I don't want to keep you long" Steve said, "but I do want to thank you all for the effort you put in this afternoon." They went on to have a discussion on the progress made and planning the next meeting. They also shared lessons learned. Steve suggested that although all of these meetings might err on the side of painful, he felt they were a way of learning about each other and opening up the communication channels.

"I am sure you will hear that some people see this as a bit of a waste of time, but we need to think about all the time we are spending right now as an investment, where the payback would come later."

Steve then said, "as an idea I would like to go around each of you and do a "pro's and con's." Can each of you give me one thing that you think was good about this meeting and one thing we could do better next time.

	Pro	Con
Judy	See the degree of agreement	The pain of discussion
Sarah	People willing to open up	Obvious buried issues
Holly	Combined teams together	Emotional
Mina	Glad we had a facilitator	Little out of comfort zone
Steve	Honesty / emotion	Not enough time

Sarah then suggested to the team that, given the goal of building better relationships between people, maybe in future they could go around the table at the end of each meeting and evaluate the meeting on task vs. relationship. "What exactly do you mean?" Mina asked.

"Typically, in business we think we are being productive when we focus on the task - the 'job at hand.' In this case it was to get agreement on the values. That was our task - the purpose of the meeting. But if you are all trying to shift the organization to being more people-centric and work on building relationships, then it might be valuable to see whether or not when you get together to talk about task, you actually remember that you work together through relationships. If you scored every meeting on each dimension, you could self assess the degree to which things were changing. It would also remind everybody of the need to BOTH achieve your task but do so in a relationship focused manner."

"That's an interesting approach" Holly responded. "We could then actually have some objective measurement to see if we were putting our values into action. Sounds like a great idea."

Steve suggested, "as an experiment let's do a quick round the table using a score of between one and five for each aspect of task and relationship". The results seemed to show that while the task scored higher, there was some time committed to relationship building. What was probably on everyone's mind, was the issue that Jean had raised.

"Exactly," Sarah said. "If you had just shut Jean down or not allowed Steve to express his feelings or even come down hard on Liz for her comments, we would have made little progress on the relationship side – we might even had made it worse and confirmed some peoples fears. But I would suggest to you that because we took the time to de-escalate the situation and look at the personal feelings behind it, we were investing time in relationship building. It's interesting if we look at the pros and cons several of the cons related to the discomfort of the relationship portion of the meeting. In my mind allowing that to happen was a big pro."

Soon after they wrapped up the meeting. It was agreed that Sarah's ideas were valuable and that maybe they would start to assess meeting performance on this basis more widely in the future. There was also agreement that having Sarah as a facilitator was critical for success, and in the future this might be something that should be continued.

THOUGHTS AND IDEAS

1. Steve is correct to worry about bringing together his leadership team and the culture change team. Creating tension and a forum for disagreement is the only way issues can be discussed and resolved.

2. Asking about personalities before the meeting is a valuable way of preparing for issues that may arise.

3. Sometimes people seen as "troublemakers" are those an organization needs – they speak out and tell the truth as they see it. They can grow into most valuable allies once they believe.

4. Again, the process may be slow and painful – but what power consensus can create if leaders and their people know they are on the same path.

5. The words being used are important and the time taken to obtain agreement is a valuable investment.

6. The advantage of an independent facilitator can be seen when emotions escalate. The Liz / Jean situation worked out well as an issue was raised, resolved and the air cleared.

This mutual development of the values for Great Toys is powerful. The words are relevant to all, and this base can then be used for operational implementation. The session, although there was a clear "task" involved also served to help develop the values and behaviours of individuals and the groups. Typically, team development is not really "tested by fire" until the team is observed working on a task where disagreements have to be resolved.

7 Developing new partners

Once again Steve had returned home for the weekend and had time to relax and talk things over with Jenny. They had discussed the Friday afternoon meeting with the two groups about the values and Jenny had provided some insight into the challenges to expect in building a trust based relationship across the organization. He told her about the "white flag" example, and she had laughed and agreed.

"It's one of the problems in the business reformation that is happening. Business moves at such a fast pace these days and taking the time to focus on the soft stuff, as they say, is often seen as a distraction and a waste of time. It is made worse by the fact that there are massive hidden costs of a poor culture, but no one can connect the dots. Because of that, no one understands the ROI from investing in effective human integration."

Steve smiled. "Yes, I remember - in fact Liz talked to me about the similarity to quality management. It wasn't until people started to realize the hidden financial impact of poor quality that they started to invest in problem prevention activities."

"But it's more than financial damage. Peoples whole lives are being damaged" Jenny added. "We know workplace stress has risen but its' back to your white flag story. You'd be amazed at what people put up with, they just keep their heads down and do what they are told. They worry about mortgages, credit cards, kids education and they just hunker down. That impacts their families, the community; the local society - everything."

"What a waste of human talent and human potential" Steve replied.

"Yes and I'll tell you one other thing Steve. There's a lot of businesses out there paying lip service around all of these changes that are needed - climate change and society issues. I know because some of them are my clients. They want quick fixes, the 'silver bullet.' Just come in a give me a program to change my culture and we can get back to business. Doesn't work that way. They even have names for it – social washing and green washing."

"I think you are right," Steve replied. "I was just reading something by Paul Polman[iii] who used to be CEO of Unilever who spent years building a whole business eco-system both within the company and with its external partners, only to see it all threatened by what appeared to be an attractive corporate takeover by Kraft Heinz. Money still seems to rank ahead of responsible business."

Steve was starting to realize that the direction he was headed in with the business would be open to criticism. Not just from people internally who didn't have time for building the necessary people focus, but also from some members of the board and others such as the bank. It was going to be a balancing act. Lots of people were talking about integration and ESG and all these new ways that business would be more responsible. But the reality was that many of them were just shuffling the deck chairs around on the Titanic. Real change required a true reformation of the way business was run. Not tinkering around the edges. If Great Toys was going to survive, there had to be real change and he was committed to see that through and leave a more effective, responsible, and sustainable business as his legacy.

The coming week at the office was going to be hectic. The new toys had to be ready. The toy show was imminent, and they had to be there with a splash to get the new orders. Operations had to be gearing up to get the product out to meet what they hoped would be an influx of new orders.

Marketing had to be there to support the launch of the product, as well as building Great Toys presence on social media. He knew that Charlene also wanted him to start getting more involved with the community designers that had become partners in the launch of the new designs - primarily because the plans were that local design support would start to become a key feeder route for future product.

This week would also require Steve to follow up on his contacts with the customers and the suppliers, that they were building enhanced relationships with. They already had one of their suppliers working with them on new product ideas and Steve needed to develop that relationship. The same was true for the customers, especially since Steve had started to build relationships with several of these since his one-on-one phone calls with their CEO's, after Gord Mason, his previous director of sales had to step down from his position.

Finally, Steve needed to follow up with Tony on the IT situation. He had left this as a low priority, but they really did need to decide a strategy for bringing the digital world into the core of their operating capability. The more Steve had thought about it the more he was convinced that a director of IT was NOT what they needed. One of the core aspects of competitive advantage now, was the ability to collect, store and access information that enhanced organizational knowledge. He needed someone who understood the capability of digital technology but more importantly, someone who could support their whole team on how best to use knowledge as a key business asset. That was not a "techy" but a business person with an IT background. Maybe he needed to talk to Simon about this - after all, that was his background, as Steve had discovered when he met with him to talk about the board challenges.

When Steve arrived at the office on Monday, he had committed the whole morning to product issues. He and Charlene were to meet and discuss progress and would then go and visit with the local design team that Charlene had been working with. The discussions at the office went well.

Things were on track, so they headed out to Steve's car for the drive to meet with the community based designers.

On the way, they had a chance to chat, and Charlene thought this would be a good time to float an idea.

"I have to tell you these people are really excited to be working with us Steve" she started. "There is a good feeling about a local firm teaming up with local entrepreneurs to combine their capabilities."

"You have made great progress Charlene" Steve replied. "I must admit it has been a bit of a stretch for everyone because this so different from anything we have done before. Do you think there is a future with this sort of arrangement?"

"Well, that's what I wanted to talk with you about. How willing are we to go deeper into our commitment to the community?" Charlene asked.

"Rebuilding our commitment to the community is an important goal" Steve responded. "I have already talked with Holly about re-energizing the social club and supporting those initiatives."

"What I have in mind is a lot more substantial Steve. I don't know whether I am over-reaching or dreaming or hallucinating or what, but I feel so positive about what we have done in the last few months that I can see significant potential in the future. But it would be very different."

Steve laughed "now you have me worried" he replied. But as I was recently told there is no progress without risk. What do you have in mind?"

"My idea will require making our involvement with the community a central pillar of our business. Here's what I have been thinking about. First we need to look at establishing a framework that brings community potential and Great Toys together. I would call it 'Partners in Play."

"I love the sound of that" Steve replied, "but what do you see the framework being?"

"I think we have to take it slow and build out from this work we are doing now" Charlene said. "First, I think we establish a design award and shared development program through which we build a pipeline of new design ideas into my group. I don't need employees, but I need access to people with ideas who we can help and support. Whether they actually work for us or not is not really material these days."

"I like that. What then?" Steve replied.

"You have to ask yourself where these people come from, and the answer in many cases is the local vocational schools or universities depending on their levels or qualifications. So, what if we were to partner with one or more local schools or universities?"

"Generally, I like the idea but to what end - why would we want to do that?"

"There are at least two reasons. First on the design side we would further reinforce the pipeline idea, while bringing us even closer to the state of the art thinking at the front end of the design process. That could give us a competitive edge and it would also allow us to build early relationships with up and coming students. We might even try and get some government support for funding apprenticeship schemes or day release or co-operative programs."

"It sounds good but what about timing and financial commitments? Isn't it too early for this?" Steve asked.

"My thinking is that we look at next September as the next intake at the schools. First we would start small with the vocational schools focusing on design. Funding would be a combination of government support and a portion of the royalty revenues that would start to flow from using the local designs. The key is to start small but get our name out there. It would be a great feeder pipeline and it would build our community reputation."

"So, what about universities - what are you thinking about there?" Steve asked.

"I have gone a little out of my depth or boundaries here" Charlene replied. "But I spoke with Julia Stevens - remember she is the lady in sales who has a strong background in education. We thought that maybe the university linkage might be broader than design. Julia believes that we have an opportunity to carve a unique niche in the market by really building the linkage between toys and education. If we could find a way of partnering with the educational faculty and building a linkage that strengthens the connection between learning, play and toys, Julia thinks we could position ourselves in the serious thinkers who are looking for toys for more than entertainment reasons."

"Amazing" Steve replied. "I really think you have the basis of both a great local design strategy but also a major way of embedding the company back as part of the community. This approach, assuming we can make it work, is way better than just supporting local charities. This actually helps build the community. I agree that we take it slow - but you have my blessing to investigate this some more and develop both a short term as well as a longer term plan. Once you have something let's share it with the leadership team and see what they think. This might be a great opportunity to start our partnership circle approach."

By now they had arrived at the old warehouse district where the designers had their office. As he walked into the location where the meeting was to be held, he almost thought he was stepping back in time to his own design company. The way things looked, the way people were talking and inter-acting, the whole feel of the place was one of positive energy. He smiled to himself. This was what he eventually hoped Great Toys would feel like.

Steve was introduced to the team of people around the table who were clearly enthusiastic about the relationship that Charlene had been building with them. It turned out that Maria Fernandez had been the appointed team leader of the independent designers group; she welcomed Steve and ran them through the history of both the team and its overall work as well as the project of working with Great Toys. She left no doubt in Steve's mind that they were committed to a deeper and developing relationship.

"You seem to have done some really great work" Steve said. "Both you and your team as well as Charlene's team from Great Toys. I am looking forward to building this relationship. Let me ask you, is there anything you need or are concerned about that I can help with?"

Maria replied, "so far things have been very open but obviously one thing we are concerned about working with a company is that someone will just change their mind and everything we develop together will either disappear or you will keep using our ideas but stop sharing the benefits."

"So, it's a matter of both having an agreement written down but also trust?" Steve replied.

"Yes" Maria responded. "Some of our people have worked for large companies and the reason they started out on their own, was that although they loved the work, they couldn't stand the climate. As creative people they often need to have fun and flexibility and managements approach was too rigid. They felt hemmed in and controlled - and often not appreciated. They just didn't like the way companies operated."

"As far as agreements are concerned, didn't you already put something in writing with Charlene and our legal team?" Steve asked.

Maria laughed as did several of her team. "Let's be fair" she replied "we all know legal agreements can be open to some level of interpretation, and you have deeper pockets than we do. If you wanted to, you could tie us up in legal arguments forever."

Now it was Steve's turn to laugh, "absolutely right - but I think if we resorted to having to get the lawyers involved, we would be well past trust and partnering anyway. What can we do to build the trust?"

"The main thing is being open and fair in dealing with us and making sure we have good communications continually," Maria replied. "What we really want, is a partnership where we build our relationship so that it goes deep."

Steve thought for a moment and then opened up his laptop. "Let me show you something we are working on. There are two things - first the business model where we talk about both suppliers and community. How would that piece work for you?" They all crowded round the laptop to read the Great Toys values; the two most relevant phrases were:

Working with suppliers in a sustainable, mutually beneficial manner
Respecting and contributing to society and the communities we operate

Steve continued, "the other piece is what we call 'Stakeholder Values' and our idea is that it is a set of behavioural beliefs that we want to be judged against with people like yourselves." At that point Steve showed them the document that was a work in progress, which they were going to try and agree on internally later in the week.

"These look really great" Maria replied. Some other members of her group also asked questions. "But how would we make sure you were living up to this?"

Steve considered for a minute then answered, "my thoughts at the moment are that we will need to develop some metrics to evaluate ourselves against these specific statements. Maybe once a month you could tell us how we are doing and as part of the communications we would sit down together and work through the responses and see where we could improve. How does that sound?"

The group felt this would be very helpful and would reflect a true "relationship building" approach. It was agreed that this would be a very positive approach, and that they could pilot and develop this together - starting as of now. It would go well beyond simple statements, to actually being the basics for accountability and assessment of performance on both sides.

This discussion seemed to have added to the positive feeling of the group, and the meeting ended after some more discussion. On the way back to the office Charlene suggested that the approach being developed with this design group as a pilot, should be shared with the leadership team and maybe could form the basis of developing a broader based model of "relationship health" across key suppliers. It could also form the basis of thinking on customer relationships. As Charlene said

"There is no point developing all of these statements unless we are prepared to hold ourselves accountable. To do that we need a set of measures that allow key stakeholders to rate us. If we do that we can build our credibility and turn the words into reality. We can build the trust and also focus on solving issues and searching new ways to do things. Win, Win I would say?"

Steve laughed "seriously Charlene, this has been a great start. Let's tell the leadership team about it and you can lead the charge."

"Hmm. I will have to watch this" Charlene replied. "What is it they say, never volunteer!."

That afternoon Steve had a working session with Liz to follow up on ramping up operational readiness for the new toys, as well as a visit to the key supplier that they were working with for a new toy design. This was the second initiative that Charlene had suggested and given that it was supplier focused and involved materials, Liz was now managing the relationship. Steve was a bit surprised when Liz seemed to be reacting to him a bit strangely.

"Is there anything up that is bothering you, which we need to talk about?" he asked.

"I was trying to think how to bring it up with you Steve, and yes, there is."

"Let me have it," Steve replied, "and I promise to hear you out."

"It's about budgets" Liz started. "I have been arguing with Tony because he thinks he can just reallocate budget funds that were earmarked for my department, just because I haven't spent them yet, and it's really upsetting me. I don't see it as being, as we are supposed to be aiming at, cooperative or collaborative. I thought this was my money. So that's the reason I am brooding. He told me you had agreed."

Steve smiled to himself, remembering his conversation with Tony on this very subject.

"Help me understand a bit Liz. When you say it's 'your money' what do you mean, because I am not sure it is, or ever was your money?"

Liz seemed a bit surprised with Steve's reply and started to get a little more defensive.

"It's my money because once budgets are agreed that amount is in my pot, and I manage my operations within that budget. It doesn't make sense to have a budget approved and then someone just arbitrarily takes the money away again."

"So, what you are saying" Steve replied, "if I understand correctly, is that once we have divvied up all the money in the budget, if something changes and there is a more important priority somewhere else then it would be Tony's responsibility to find the money and not take it out of your allocations even if you haven't used it yet?"

"That's exactly what I mean" Liz confirmed. "As a senior manager its' my job to manage within my budget. If I have underspent in one area then it's up to me to decide where to reallocate the funds."

"Ah, OK I get it," Steve replied. "Do you think the other managers on the team feel the same way about their budgets?"

"Yes, I think that is exactly how most of them think - although its' never come up as a discussion before. Why? Do you think I'm wrong?"

"I certainly have a different opinion to you Liz" Steve replied. "I'm not sure I would say you were outright wrong. It would be a great discussion to have with the whole team I think. Leave it with me. But I am glad you raised it. Right or wrong I now know it is an issue for you and we need to work it out. So, I commit to coming back to you on this - now that's out of the way how are the supplier relationships going on the new product innovation?"

Liz outlined for Steve all the actions that were being taken, and some of the key milestones they had been able to achieve. She confirmed that both this product as well as the other three areas that Charlene were working on, were being integrated into operational scheduling and at the moment they were confident that the volumes forecast by sales would be delivered on schedule to meet the Christmas delivery deadlines.

"It takes some getting used to, realizing that we work about a year ahead of other people" Steve remarked. "I have trouble getting used to our Christmas delivery season being in the summer." Once they finished up at the office, they drove to the supplier that Liz and Charlene had been working with.

Steve had spoken with the CEO of the supplier by phone, but the main contacts had been Charlene and Liz. Steve knew that this was an entrepreneurial start up company in its' early days. Charlene had originally indicated that their interest in working with Great Toys came from not wanting to get into toy production but in developing new materials that can be used for safer play.

Even with this knowledge Steve was surprised that they finally pulled up in a very run-down and shabby looking warehouse. There was no one at reception so they rang the bell on the desk and a man came running out wearing a white lab coat with his hair dishevelled, and a smile all over his face.

"Welcome to our humble home" he said as he shook hands with Steve. "You must be Mr. Steve Eccles - we spoke on the phone? It is a great pleasure to have you visit us. We are so enjoying working with your people."

"Ah yes" Steve replied. "We did talk on the phone some weeks ago; I remember - it was Mr. Sharmine was it not?"

"Yes, yes" he replied, "but please call me Abdul. Strange name yes? You may guess that I was not born in England. I came from Syria as an immigrant."

With little ceremony he ushered them through into the operational part of the warehouse. Steve was at once blown away with two things. The quality of the work environment and equipment that the company had, was state of the art - something any well to do company would be proud to have. The second thing he felt was the "fun" of the place. Clearly people were busy, but everyone was smiling, and appeared to be cooperating, experimenting, trying things. It almost had the feel of a common room in a university.

It turned out that Abdul Sharmine was raised in Syria but he and his family, wife and three children, had lost everything when they fled as refugees. He had started his business a few years ago, with financial support from both friends and his local community but also a small seed capital fund. Abdul was, it turned out a highly qualified engineer who had a passion for inventing things and had already come up with several ideas which had been patented and sold to others who were able to exploit the ideas.

"I am so glad we have the opportunity to work with Great Toys" he had explained. "I have had a number of bad experiences with people who think because I am an immigrant, I don't understand anything about the law and other things. That was the reason I wanted to make sure that when we started out we chose both a privately owned business where I could get to know the owners personally; it was also the reason why we were so cautious and wanted to make sure all the commitments and paperwork were in place before we showed and shared what we were doing. I have had so many unethical people think they can steal my ideas, but I have to stay positive."

Steve was starting to really like this enthusiastic individual. The tour continued and Liz spent some time with the technical people, ironing out some operational issues. Steve was able to spend time with Abdul and learn more about his business and his ideas. By the time Liz was ready to leave, Steve had arranged with Abdul for an exchange visit where he would come and have a tour of Great Toys. As he was leaving Abdul made the point that he was so appreciative of Steve taking the time to come, and that his support of smaller, growing, entrepreneurial business was a very valuable service to the community. "All we ask is to be given a chance" was what Abdul had said a number of times.

"What do you think about Abdul and his business?" Steve asked Liz, as they headed back to the office.

Liz laughed "Well it certainly is 'what you see is what you get" she said. "I must admit I was taken back the first time I went there, but I have to tell you Steve, that is a group of very talented and ambitious people that Abdul has assembled. They are passionate about the work that they are doing and about being part of the team."

"What about their image though" Steve asked, "it did look a bit shabby you must admit?"

"From what I gather" Liz replied, "Abdul makes the point that money should be spent on things that create value. Getting and keeping talented people and giving them the equipment that they need to do the job. One of them said to me that Abdul sees his role as the facilitator. His job is to put things in place, remove any barriers and let people get on with what they need to do. She said they try to keep it simple."

"Sounds like a solid way to build a reputation. I suppose the other things can come later" Steve replied.

Keep it simple thought Steve. Great philosophy. Wonder if we asked our people would they think that was what we did. I wonder what barriers exist to just "winding them up and letting them go?"

Lot's to think about - but one thing Steve came away with was a feeling that this relationship might possibly grow into something very rewarding for both organizations.

The more Steve got out and started to work with community and other partners, the more ideas seemed to be generated. The challenge was that Steve knew he had to remain focused on the few key things that were critical for short term survival and longer term development and growth.

THOUGHTS AND IDEAS

1. What Steve is doing may be seen as counter cultural. He is not looking for a quick fix to the business, as success is based on a sound underlying business model. This is what he is building.
2. "Fixing" or changing culture can be met with suspicion, so the expression of mistrust from "outsiders" is not unusual.
3. Starting to work with stakeholders like community and suppliers often opens up opportunities for new thinking.
4. Often, in showing commitment, Great Toys and Steve have to take the first step in being open and taking risks.
5. The more the stakeholder network grows the broader will be the ideas and opportunities. Focus must be balanced with opportunities for innovation.
6. Measures / metrics for monitoring effective collaboration and "partnerships" should be developed mutually.
7. Trust is a foundation for behaviour. Liz didn't want to give up her budget because "she knew what happened last time."
8. Sometimes working with "innovative and creative" people takes you out of your "comfort zone." This is good – it is how people and organizations grow.

"Empowering" people on Steve's team to re-develop relationships with others in their "network" is a powerful approach to their personal development. As each of them develops a portion of the business model, they develop personal ownership to their collective success.

Fun Returns to Great Toys

8 Closing the gaps

By mid week it was time to revisit the joint meeting with the Culture Change Team, to start to focus on action items. Mina had already contacted Steve to let him know that her team had spent some time comparing the draft stakeholder values statement created by the leadership team with the behavioural values that were agreed at the last meeting. While they had finally confirmed that the existing draft could be used "as is," Mina did tell Steve that the process had been a challenge.

"What we are all learning in this process Steve, is that achieving complete agreement is usually impossible. When we were working on the values originally we had started voting on certain things to decide what was acceptable, but then we got into trying to define was an acceptable majority should be 75%? 51%? The problem was that we started to think about voting on the voting. It was getting ridiculous. So, we asked for some advice from Holly and that totally changed things."

"That sounds like it was profound. What was the advice Holly had" Steve asked?

"The main thing was that voting of any type in these situations can be a problem. Voting creates winners and losers. It also sets up a situation where people start to 'trade votes' - you give me this one and I will give you that one. So, we asked Holly what alternative there was, and she suggested that complete agreement was unnecessary as long as people were prepared to talk things through and arrive at consensus - this being the ability to support something that they may have some reservations about, but where their voice had been heard and their arguments put forward and where the majority of the team clearly felt an alternative decision was more viable."

"But surely there are some issues where one or more people just cannot agree, where they see things differently. How do you resolve those where consensus can't be achieved?" Steve asked.

"Holly suggested that in these cases the team as a whole would have to arrive at agreement that consensus was not possible and defer any decision. That sounds like potential for disaster I know - but we were surprised at what happened. Because disagreement was considered such a serious issue, a failure for us as a group, that any decision would be completely deferred, it brought the team to a clear focus on their collective responsibility to get the job done. The result was that people tried harder. They listened better. They put forward better arguments. They went in search of facts to support their position. It actually enhanced the process."

"That is great" Steve replied. "I know about the concept of consensus, but what I have seen in the past is that where a team cannot decide then the leader steps in a takes over. I always thought that was what needed to happen?"

Mina laughed "Holly told us exactly that. She explained that the danger of that approach is that eventually the team members start to wonder why they are bothering and look to the leader to be told what to do. The risk is that when a leader steps in like that, they potentially take away the teams accountability and responsibility."

"But surely" Steve asked "there are some situations where deferring the decision can't be allowed to happen? Leadership at the end of the day is getting things done. How can a leader just stand by and wait?"

Again, Mina chuckled, "of course you are absolutely right. Certain situations cannot be allowed to be deferred. But whose problem is it? The teams. They were given responsibility and accountability and clearly were unable to complete the task. It is THEY who then need to approach their leader and explain that they cannot reach a decision and would like some help."

"So doesn't that amount to the same thing?" Steve asked.

"Not really - I think you will see there is a difference here. At that point the situation is reviewed and, with the clear support of the team, the leader steps into the decision making role. A CLEAR message has been sent. You, the team, were given the opportunity to recommend a course of action and couldn't. The leader has been given a teaching moment to review the team's deliberations, maybe identify points that were not dealt with and illustrate that, given a decision must be made, what risks the leader recognizes in deciding a course of action."

This conversation raised issues about team development and decision making dynamics that Steve hadn't considered before. He reflected that once again, anybody can put teams in place and talk about team work and decision making, but it the operational reality of how you actually make it work that either builds or depletes the desired culture. This was clearly a key link between the adoption of team thinking and the need for changes in the way managers and leaders operated.

Fortunately, the Wednesday follow-up meeting was more of an input and clarification session, with the culture change team providing input to management. They had agreed on the behavioural values at this point, so the CCT was reporting back on their research and discussion, especially related to action and implementation. This had identified there were clear gaps between the behaviour they had all now agreed they wanted to aspire to, and what the reality was. These gaps were seen by the employees and others such as suppliers and customers (even though the team indicated that given the short time, only a sample of the latter had been possible).

Prior to the start of the meeting, it had been agreed that trying to review every aspect where there were perceived gaps would not be a good use of time; the CCT had been asked to present what they considered the top ten, and their ideas to reduce this down to the top five that would form the foundation of the first improvement phase. Later phases would be developed under the concept of continual improvement.

The team explained that to determine the critical issues they had returned to the original general discussions and reviewed all the notes. They had then decided to try and focus on the specific "words" from the final list that had been the basis of the presentation and discussion with the board. They presented the list as a reminder:

Trusting	Supportive	Positive
Open	Cooperative	Collaborative
Fun	Fair	Honest
Sharing	Challenging	Equality
Ethical	Caring	Authentic
Competent	Inclusive	Safe
Diverse	Accountable	Considerate
Responsible		Respectful

When the team started the presentation, the following items had the lowest ratings based on employee input. Trust, fun, ethical, collaborative, supportive, fair, inclusive, respectful, authentic, and safe. The team also made the point that although it was not a "value" per se, clarity of purpose was a problem that needed to be fixed. The CCT had showed the updated "purpose statement" to many employees, and this had been well received but it had generated a discussion about "well, what does this mean to me in my job?" Based on this input the members of CCT suggested some work needed to be done in this area.

There was a lot of discussion about these ten items, including a growing challenge of agreeing on what the words <u>*actually meant*</u>. People talked about things like trust being an outcome rather than a value, and about things like collaboration and cooperation really meaning the same thing. Eventually it was agreed that the following would be the high priority items for starting the needed changes. Each item is shown with its score as seen from the input.

Value	1	2	3	4	5	6	7	8	9	10
Respectful	▓	▓	▓	▓	▓					
Safe workplace	▓	▓								
Fair / inclusive	▓	▓								
Collaborative	▓	▓	▓							
Ethical	▓	▓	▓	▓						

Both teams were beginning to see that many values were interconnected; as an example, respectful, inclusive, and collaborative were all related to how people felt they were being treated. A safe workplace was connected to these three because the outcome of being treated badly was often a decline in mental health, leading to absenteeism and in a few cases long term disability. (It also led to less collaboration and respect as people became more stressed out - so it was becoming a self reinforcing circle). The team had decided that "ethical" needed to be on the list because it should be considered zero tolerance (as was a safe workplace as a goal) and there had already been clear cases of ethical lapses that both reduced morale as well as increased market place risk.

"Well, if you ask me" Jean Lewinski suggested, "it all once again comes back to leadership training. There are people in management positions that are dinosaurs. If we want to change how people are treated we need to start there."

It went a bit quiet after Jean made the comments. Body language was interesting, people looking around to see who would put up an argument. Holly was first to jump in.

"I think you may be right, " Holly replied. "The greatest interaction with people is the one-on-one that they have with their manager everyday. But are you staying all our managers are bad? Or some? Or a few? We need a bit more focus here."

"Oh, I agree its not all managers - in fact some are really good and dealing effectively with people seems just to be part of who they are. It is the few exceptions that do the damage" Jean replied.

"What would we need to do to start there, Holly?" Steve asked.

Holly replied, "it goes back to something we already talked about as part of the HR development. We need to do a better job of both hiring, developing, and evaluating everybody in a management or supervisory position on their people skills. Honestly I am convinced that part of the problem is that no one has called them out on their behaviour."

Mina jumped in "I agree but I also think that is why we need to roll out these expectations about values and behaviour as fast as possible. We cannot have anyone - managers or anybody else, saying they didn't know what was expected."

Now it was John, the new director of marketing that jumped in. "I can't believe that people don't know what acceptable behaviour is. Surely we should expect people to know how to act?"

Again, Holly responded "you are partly right John, but you have to remember many peoples definition of acceptable behaviour is based on their upbringing - where they were born, who their parents were, where they lived, what sort of attitudes they developed based on their own personal background. They can even develop perceptions of what our expectations are, when they see what people around them are doing. We have to be more careful these days as our workforce becomes more diverse. We cannot just take that for granted."

Steve asked, "so this would require that we have a mandatory orientation or, I think it's called onboarding system, so that people we hire know our expectations on day one?"

"Yes," Holly replied, "but we also need a better way of understanding the people we are hiring or even promoting. At the moment, mainly because of cost cuts, the only thing we do is some very basic testing and references. These have been hard to rely on because of the increasing privacy laws. We need to try and dig a little deeper."

"OK" Steve replied, "I think there are a number of initiatives that we need to focus on going forward. What else do you think we need to address in order the close these gaps. For example, your chart suggest we only score three out of ten when it comes to a safe workplace and safe / inclusive. I don't know about the rest of you but that seems terrible to me."

There was general agreement around the table, and it seemed that this level was more of a surprise to the leadership team members; there was some defensiveness around the results and some heated discussion about "things can't be as bad as you are suggesting" but overall, the tone remained constructive - especially when Steve supported Mina's position that the "numbers are what they are - they may not be 100% accurate but this is what people's perceptions are."

Another member of Mina's team started a discussion saying "this whole experience has been excellent for both our culture change team as well as people we engaged with. One of the things I think we should do is try and build this type of collaborative approach into the broader way that we operate and do business."

"How do you think we might do that" Liz asked?

Josh the director of sales jumped in "based on my experience working with John and Charlene on these new product initiatives, I think we need to look for every opportunity we can get to move the way we work, to a more collaborative focused approach rather than relying on functional responsibility. Ultimately it's all about relationships. If people understand the organizational purpose and are given clear responsibility and authority, it seems to me that we should wind them up and let them go."

There was laughter around the table at this suggestion.

"That is a pretty significant shift" Liz replied. "Surely we still need to have things managed through our managerial hierarchy. Won't that dilute our own authority? My fear would be that we give up responsibility but remain stuck with accountability. That might mean giving up some level of control."

Steve looked thoughtful. "That's an interesting dilemma Liz. Maybe that is the trade-off we make on engagement? As management we need to demonstrate our trust in our people by actually giving up some level of control? As long as we clearly define expectations and are there to help, support and coach as needed, then we would be shifting our management role to more of a focus on leadership?"

Again, there was some ongoing discussion around this point, until the subject of ethics and problems in the workplace were raised. Again, another of Mina's CCT started the conversation.

"The challenge for us is knowing what to do when we have a values problem or an ethical problem. If the supervisor *is* the problem, then obviously there is limited chance of resolution if we raise the issue?"

"Not really" Steve replied. "Your supervisor, if they are working the way that we expect, should be open to honest feedback."

"That's a nice theory" Mina replied, "but it is well proven that this doesn't always happen. Even if we agree it might improve, we still need a better way of dealing with this type of issue. Some sort of whistle blowing or escalation process maybe?"

"Maybe," Holly replied. "Steve and I have actually talked about this, but the problem is that a 'one size fits all' solution is going to either be too slow and bureaucratic or raise things to a level that may not be necessary. I think we need a hybrid approach that can be scaled to be fast and fair on smaller issues but reach a higher level on more serious problems."

"Do you have any thoughts yet, on how we might do that?" Steve asked.

"I would like to work with Mina's team to think this through" Holly replied, "but I am thinking we set up something like a council of your peers or an advisory circle or something like that, which would be a first level of appeal. We need something that is aimed at dealing in facts, removing emotions and being transparent. Needs some thought."

"OK we can put that on the action agenda" Steve replied. "However, I am concerned about the ethical issues as we all know these can be problematic. Given that we want to establish zero tolerance, maybe we could again set up a more senior council for this and have this specific type of issue come straight to that level?"

Again, the conversation went on and it was agreed that Holly would follow up on this. At this point they recapped the number of core action plans that needed to be put in place. Steve asked Holly to work with Mina to develop specific projects and identify the resources that were needed.

When it was clear that everyone was happy with the outcome, Steve went around the table asking each person if they had anything to add, and about their pro's and con's for the meeting. The results appeared positive, and people apparently felt that the whole meeting had an equal focus on getting through the tasks but also remaining aware of the relationships. They felt that this process would be usefully expanded to other meetings as a way of reinforcing the behaviours and values as well as trying to improve and enhance meetings. Needless to say, there had been some grumblings about the amount of time this whole process was taking, yet people didn't want to dilute the focus, but preferred to look for ways to make it more productive.

The next day Steve's agenda included a visit to the location of the customer they were working with on the new product ideas. He had worked with Josh to set up this visit, which at this stage was more of a courtesy call, as most of the design and production development work had already taken place. Their goal was to build on this relationships to see whether increased partnering on market place issues and new ideas could be developed.

Josh had also suggested that maybe it would be a good idea for Steve to also make a call on another customer, who would be close to where they were going. Great Toys had lost this client about two years ago, and they now flatly refused to do business with them. Josh had been unable to get in but when he had suggested that his CEO would like to visit and hear the reasons first-hand, it was agreed that the director of purchasing would give him "a short time."

To say it was a frosty reception would be an understatement. The company was a large distributor of toys to the retail market and had been a long time customer of Great Toys until they finally dropped them as a supplier two years ago. Steve and Josh were kept waiting for some time - but exercised patience as they realized they had little leverage or expectation of being welcomed. They were finally shown into the directors office who welcomed them and offered coffee - but it was clearly all business.

"So" he started, "how can I help you today?"

Steve started out with the pleasantries and then went on to apologize for the events that had apparently led to their being dumped as a supplier. He ended with "as you know I have taken over as CEO from my brother and we are really trying to change things and solve the problems we had. Josh has taken over sales as you know, and personally I was hoping that maybe once we are back on track we would have a chance at becoming a supplier again?"

The Director still had a stoic, serious look on his face as he leant forward and said "Steve, sorry to burst your bubble but if you were the last toy supplier in this country I would never do business with you again."

"Oh," Steve replied - a bit taken aback by the bluntness of the response. His face obviously showed it.

"Look Steve, I've no doubt you found a lot of problems when you took over and I have no doubt that you are committed to fixing them. But I have to tell you, two years ago when we dropped you, it was a tough decision, but I had no option. Your service and quality had been declining for some time. My problems were met with offers to drop the price on the next order and take me out to dinner. But here's the problem. Your company let me down. I let my own company down. Our customers were depending on us to supply them but all we received were promises. I needed product. I needed a responsible supplier. Someone I could trust to come through for me. I failed because of you. That is a risk I am never going to take again - so I'm sorry but there we are."

The conversation soon ended, as it was clear that their time was over. They bid farewell and left.

As Steve and Josh were driving away, Steve asked Josh his thoughts. He laughed "well at least I think we received the honest truth" he said.

"What did we learn" Steve asked?

"I think we had Sales 101 repeated to us Steve. At the end of the day customers want it all. Great product. Great price. Great service. The whole package. The days of trading off price, quality and service are way behind us. We need to think about our customers as partners who are dependent upon us and we need to take that seriously, including acting when we fall short. A loyal customer is a valuable asset that takes a lot of investment to build and nurture but which can be lost, and not easily recovered."

"Agreed," Steve confirmed. "It would be interesting for our people to hear the sort of thing we heard today. It certainly makes it both real, serious and 'in your face.' You really get to appreciate what a critical part we play in their supply chain."

"Maybe we can and should do that" Josh added.

"How do you mean?" Steve asked.

"We need to build out our relationships with key customers in particular" Josh replied. "We need to look for multiple contact points where people other than sales and accounting have client connections. If we did that we could actually monitor the quality of our key relationships in the future on a more objective basis. My guess would be that if operations knew that we were in jeopardy of losing the account, we would see greater internal traction."

"Maybe once we get things up and running more effectively with marketing, that could be one of our goals," Steve suggested. "You and John could work on looking at the CRM system and developing it so that all departments have access. Maybe we could even link this in with our social media plans and jointly promote our customers as part of our own visibility."

They continued the discussion as they headed to the next call with their customer who was to become a "future partner" who were already heavily engaged in collaboration. Steve and Josh met with the CEO who also brought in several members of her leadership team. They talked about their own business goals and how they viewed suppliers like Great Toys as an extension of their own business. Steve was able to share the direction his company was headed and showed them the business model statement, that had been developed, pointing out both the introduction and the line related to customers:

> *People are central to building the relationships we need for a sustainable business model that achieves our company Purpose. The desired outcomes include:*
> *Serving customers needs with safe, value-based products and support*

It was agreed that both companies should put in place regular joint relationship monitoring that would ensure performance on these aspects. Steve and Josh also suggested that as they moved forward, a permanent new product development circle should be established with two people from each company who would identify, investigate, and recommend areas for joint development in the future.

The day had been an interesting contrast in addressing what happened when things went wrong with key relationships, and what opportunities existed when mutual desire to working together could develop the collaboration and cooperation needed to succeed.

THOUGHTS AND IDEAS

1. Having given Mina and her team the task of developing values and assessing the gap, Steve must give them the time to figure out the best way for taking action.
2. Mina and her teams experience on voting versus arriving at consensus is a very powerful learning experience.
3. Steve, as any leader, wants to jump in and decide to get things moving. He needs to be careful in how he behaves and what messages he gives people about trust, based on his actions.
4. The areas of "greatest pain" (the gaps) must be addressed first to start delivering on the change needed.
5. As implementation proceeds certain operational changes are becoming more apparent such as:
   a. Effective leadership commitment, action, and behaviour at all levels.
   b. Investing in areas like effective onboarding as a critical step in embedding the values and behaviours expected.
   c. Embedding cross-functional collaboration as a core approach to daily operational task execution.
   d. The need for an independent, impartial safety valve for people to raise culture / behaviour issues.
6. When partnerships fail, each party can learn about "what happened" if they are able to understand the issues from the other partners perspective. Don't argue – it is their reality.

The reason operational implementation can be slow and tedious is that it involves learning. New issues are raised and must often be added to the list of changes required.

---

9 More advice from Sarah

Steve's weekly meeting with Sarah had been delayed this week so that the joint meeting on finalizing the values could take place. When they finally met Steve brought her up to date on the progress and the success of the culture change team. He was a bit taken aback when her first thought was "what have you done to celebrate the success of their work?"

"Lesson number one in moving forward" Sarah said laughing "is to celebrate success."

"I must admit that it never crossed my mind" Steve replied.

"It's a key part of relationships building but much more than that it is part of building trust. I don't know if you remember Steve, in your business reading, but there was a famous guy that wrote "The 7 Habits of Highly Effective People" - I think his name was Stephen Covey[iv]. One of his key ideas was that building relationships is like building bank accounts - he called them the emotional bank account. He suggested that things like a 'thank you' for a job well done, or a pat on the back, or even recognition of the members of a team who have done a good job, are like deposits in the bank account. At some point, like a bank account, something negative may happen; you have to tell someone about a problem or ask a favour. These cause withdrawals from the bank account. If you never make a deposit then there are no funds to withdraw against."

"What a great concept" Steve replied. "I think we often take it for granted in business that people get paid to do their job, so why would I thank them for doing what they are supposed to do? But where we have an equal focus on sustaining an effective workplace then relationship building is critical. I guess this type of approach would also go a long way to addressing fairness and recognition and other things?"

"It also reminds me of someone I worked with once" Sarah replied. "She always said that 'when she was right no one remembered but when she was wrong no one let her forget it.' So, celebrate success."

"I suppose in business we so often think about rewards for a job well done has to be cash compensation or something tangible" Steve replied, "but in building relationships things like you suggest are equally important?"

"Not to say there isn't a place for it" Sarah responded, "but you need to have choices. Verbal acknowledgement is all that a lot of people want but some may want something more. Tickets to a local football game or a pizza night at the pub. Then there are things like recognition awards - certificates and cups and shields. Still needed of course are financial rewards. Let me ask you, how much flexibility do you give your supervisors to give rewards?"

"Interesting question" Steve replied. "I am pretty sure it's close to zero. The budgets are usually tight and there is little in the way of discretionary funds for that type of performance related 'thank you' - if I remember correctly if you want to do something like you are suggesting a supervisor needs to get permission from HR."

"That's a problem. If the first line of values based leadership is supervisors, you have to give them the tools for the job. The last thing you need is a cumbersome bureaucratic process. I know in my company there were often late night working sessions where the supervisor made the decision late at night when the work was done or even called out and ordered food as a thank you. If you have to ask permission the moment of recognition is lost forever. You may want to take a look at that?"

Steve also updated Sarah on the feverish activity the business was currently engaged in. Their new products had all successfully met the deadlines and were being displayed in the trade show for the next Christmas season about eight months away. So far order intake had been slightly better then expected and the most positive feedback had been the number of customers and other industry people who had told the company that they "were glad to see them back in business." Although controlling budgets had been a challenge they had been able to execute the whole program and remain with the expense level they had committed to the bank. Steve was able to tell Sarah that the bank seemed to be happy although obviously their ability to continue still remained a concern.

Steve then asked Sarah about the cocktail reception that they had attended some weeks ago when he had been "collared" by Paul, a local retired business person who had offered Steve help if he wanted it but with an ulterior motive of eventually having him be involved in the local venture capital fund.

"Oh yes" Sarah replied. "I remember it. Paul is a really great individual, and the venture capital activity is a core part of his life now he is retired. He loves the whole innovation and creativity thing and has a passion for understanding and working with inventive minds who have ideas. Why do you ask?"

"Two reasons" Steve replied. "First I have been having some discussions with Charlene our director of product and innovation. She has led the work on the fast track development of the new products and has done a fantastic job."

Sarah jumped in "and have you thanked her yet" she asked laughing.

"I get it - enough already" Steve replied, also laughing "I think you know the answer - I did thank her and tell her what a great job she did but yes, I will think some more about that."

"Sorry" said Sarah "please continue."

Steve did. "So, Charlene was suggesting that maybe we could start developing more in-depth partnerships with local organizations and I thought maybe Paul would have a good idea of what is out there, and how we might move forward?"

"It sounds right up his street - I am sure he would love to chat about it. What was the second reason?"

"Well, it ties in with the first" Steve replied. "Charlene suggested a strategy whereby we could bring together the development of new locally designed products with future contributions to the venture capital funding, in particular to supporting schools and colleges. This way we could really start to re-build our role in the community as well as develop a pipeline of new ideas."

"That is a fantastic idea Steve" Sarah said excitedly. "I think what I would suggest is that we set up an exploratory meeting with Paul that includes you and I as well as Charlene. We could explore her ideas and from there maybe we could put in place some sort of community collaboration group?" They then moved on to discussing the progress on their "values" and the action items.

Steve raised the importance of hiring and promotions that had come up again at the values meeting. It was clear this was going to be a key area for improvement, and it took Steve back to earlier conversations about getting the right people on the bus. Sarah told Steve of her experience at Fabrications Unlimited - where she was still a director, having sold the family business during the previous year.

"I once believed that most of this testing for people was an expensive luxury" Sarah told Steve. "But a few years ago, in fact soon after I took over from my late husband, I had some career counselling that included a number of these assessments - and the results were amazing. I was so taken with the insight that it provided, that we implemented the approach across the company. As the sophistication of the assessment tools and approaches developed, we changed suppliers but up to recently we were working with a great local company that has an amazing product."

"I have heard something about these things" Steve replied, "but from what I remember it is all about identifying people's 'types or categories,' so they can be fitted into neat little boxes. I was never very impressed with that. Interesting - but not something that you can do anything with. How did this help you?"

"First, it provided some amazing understanding of why communications go awry between people. Given that one of the major underpinnings of relationship building at all levels is effective communications, this knowledge was one of the best investments we made."

"Well, that's an issue I know" Steve laughed. "From some of the feedback that our culture change team received it was clear that misunderstandings are a key source of problems - including some of our managers not realizing that the way they say something, with no negative intent or meaning, can be totally misinterpreted and offensive to the recipient."

"That was one additional learning that we all had from doing this work, and it ties in very closely to the work you are doing on values as a foundation for expected or desired behaviour." Sarah added. "It turns out that because of the different behavioural tendencies that individuals have, some people have what are called 'blind spots' in certain areas. It is not that they are bad, it's just that they don't realize how other people see them and the way they behave."

"Not sure I understand" Steve replied. "Give me an example."

"OK" Sarah responded. "Let's use your value of 'being collaborative' as an example. Would you say that some people are better at this than others?"

"Sure" Steve replied. "In fact, that is a really important aspect of our values and one of the more important as far as I am concerned."

"So, what if you knew, at the time of hiring someone, they were naturally more or less collaborative. Would that help your decision making?" Sarah asked.

"It would certainly provide us with a great insight into the individual that we were thinking about hiring" Steve replied, "but I also see it as an early warning sign. If this person had all the technical and other skills we wanted, but was low on collaboration, we would know what to focus on with their training and development. I can see that would allow the person to get up to speed much more quickly."

"Exactly - and that is just the tip of the iceberg" Sarah replied. "This whole approach is about behavioural tendencies - _not_ trying to fit people into boxes. In fact, the math suggests that with the approach that we were using, each unique individual is similar to another person once in a hundred million chances."

"That sounds incredible" Steve said. "Is this approach expensive?"

"Don't think of it as expensive but as cost saving Steve - but let me ask you. What does it cost you when you hire the wrong person, or you don't know a person's natural tendencies and they upset the apple cart once you have hired them?"

"I really don't know" Steve replied, "but my guess would be that it could be significant."

"Let me say that based on our experience, the cost of these assessments is insignificant if you compare it to the buried financial and cultural impact of hiring the wrong person or not providing the required training and development, as well as personal coaching. It will save you money"

"If it's that good, why don't more people use it?" Steve asked.

"That I cannot tell you Steve, but I do know that the return on investment for us was significant both financially as well as the pain of having and dealing with people who were a bad fit. I think that many people fail to use it because a) they don't realize the financial impact of not knowing this information and acting on it and b) the focus on cost control often sees this as an unnecessary cost - especially when you can't show the ROI - but its not hard to figure it out."

"I think we should try it - what would be the best way of starting" Steve asked.

"What I would do Steve, is start with the leadership team, including yourself. This way you start addressing communications at the most senior level. You also set the example that you believe in this approach, as you move forward and expand the use. But even more importantly it will allow you to start the process of building relationships based on each person knowing who they really are, why they behave the way the do, and also becoming open enough, to share this with others so that they can improve their relationships."

"Plus, it will help us with our own self-development" Steve added?

"It is said that you have to know yourself before knowing others" Sarah replied. "Anybody in a leadership position today must be self-aware. They must understand their own motivations and behaviours and importantly how they appear to other people. Let me go off on a tangent here. Does Jenny your wife understand you?"

Steve laughed "Oh wow, what a question. I remember conversations when she has remarked 'sometimes I don't know who you really are' - so I would say yes, but with reservations. Why?"

"Because getting to know other people as the foundation for building relationships can be a long process," Sarah replied. "Typically, that's what we do in a marriage or any longer term personal relationship. Think about it - that's only two people and consider how complex that learning process can be. Now think about business. Multiple relationships. Changes occurring all the time. The imperative of getting up to speed quickly and adapting to change. How much more important is understanding human behaviour and tendencies in that environment?"

"Clearly very important" Steve replied, "and anything we can do to understand it better and faster has to be positive."

"Correct" Sarah responded, "and just to let you know, after we did the initial assessments with the company we used, we worked with them to expand the analytics they used, and it was even more helpful. It showed how people's behaviour changes when they are under stress, and also how people sometimes adjust their behaviour based on the environment they are in. Overall, it has been a great tool."

As the meeting ended, Sarah left the contact information with Judy to try and arrange an initial meeting with the consultant they had used, as soon as possible. As usual the conversation had been helpful to Steve but had also run on longer than planned. He was still able to check in with Tony to make sure that their financial projections remained in line, and to get an update on the sales intake and backlog that he was monitoring.

Steve felt that after his last meeting with Liz, his director of operations things had been a bit tense - especially related to the budget issues. He wanted to make sure that she was getting all the support she needed as production was at a high level of activity, ramping up to meet the deliveries that were now planned as a result of the new launch. John had also told Steve that the introduction of some initial social media boosts had resulted in a continuing growth in on-line orders.

He asked Judy to call Liz and see when he could go and see her for an update. Fortunately, Liz suggested that she and Steve got together for a quick coffee. Clearly, when they met Liz was stressed out, and Steve noticed.

"I know this is a really busy time for you Liz and I don't want to take you away for long. I just wanted to make sure that you have what you need and there are no road blocks that I can help with."

The reaction from Liz was good. "Yes Steve, I am really busy, busy, busy - but I can tell you this feels like positive stress. There has been a positive change already - there is much more of a desire to cooperate between departments. John, Josh, and I have been working closely together to monitor order intake and Charlene has been great with problem solving. In some cases, the people we are working with externally are jumping in and helping problem solve. It is great that we have a clear focus and the collaboration at our level has started to bleed down into the organization. Several of my staff have already made comments about how cooperative other departments are being."

Steve asked "I know one of the key areas that we had problems with is the customer / call centre. How have things been going there?"

"Again, more collaborative" Liz replied. "Although we do still have some underlying - how do I put it, passive / aggressive behaviour."

"How do you mean?" Steve asked.

"As you may remember, the supervisor is Janine Williams, and she still tells me she gets the feeling that some people don't think she is competent to do the job. It's just attitudes I guess - I don't know how else to explain it. She did mention to me the idea that Holly had raised with you about Janine having the opportunity to actually work on making our commitments on diversity and inclusion real. She is REALLY enthusiastic about that - and has told me she is already thinking about how she might develop case studies and run the sessions."

"The sooner we get that off the ground, the better" Steve replied. "While we are mentioning Holly, are your staffing issues been working out? I know from your plans that some of your temporary and contract staff were being called back in. Is that working OK?"

"Holly has also been just great" Liz confirmed. "My only concern is workload as she seems really busy all the time, and I have started to feel she is a bit overloaded. I know she has been putting in a lot of hours to get things done - as we all have in the ramp up."

"Thanks for the heads up" Steve replied. "I will look into that. But I assume from your response you have the staffing you need?"

Liz hesitated just for a second, but Steve noticed, and asked her to elaborate about whether there were any problems with the seasonal workforce.

"Now that you ask, yes there is a bit of a problem Steve, and I think part of the problem is created by our own policies."

"How do you mean" Steve asked.

"Many of these people have been part of the Great Toys "extended" family for years. Some only want to work part time, some have family commitments and can only work on reduced hours, yet the problem is that I think we treat them like second class citizens. We pay them less than the people they work next door to, and they have almost zero benefits; many of them just make minimum wage although the work they do is as important as the full time people we have. They are good people, and few complain because there is not much they can do about it, and we know we have leverage over them; but it just seems wrong to me."

"Another hidden legacy problem" Steve replied. "Have you talked to Holly about it?"

"Yes" Liz replied "but she tells me this is policy. I know we made a lot of these changes a few years ago when the cutbacks started but it is now the accepted practice."

"I agree Liz, its not right or fair - interesting how we have an example of yet another inconsistency with our values and our actual work practices. The challenge is going to be how we address it in the future without having too big an impact on operating costs."

"I have some ideas on that Steve, and when this panic is over, I think we need to take a hard look not just at this, but at our total work practices. Because we are a seasonal business we need a contingency workforce but there must be a better way to do it. We could also do some reallocation of resources and automate some functions, so we could take the ROI and plough it back into a fair system of compensation."

"Great" Steve replied. "Another agenda item for the future. Can I ask you to stay on top of this initiative Liz - I know we will need Holly and others involved, but in reality most of the seasonal workforce issue is in your area anyway - so you should drive it. Other than that, are we all good for the volume ramp-up?"

Liz smiled "Yes Steve, all is good. With me you can work on the basis that if you hear nothing, I am OK - if I need help I will ask."

"Super" Steve replied. "Let's leave it there. Many thanks Liz - and yell if you need help." With that they headed out, back to their respective challenges.

THOUGHTS AND IDEAS

1. Recognizing success is one of the most valuable tools to build a positive culture. Leaders are often silent on success but vocal on failure. This results in all messages being negative.
2. The concept of an emotional bank account is powerful when dealing in human relationships (of all types).
3. Trust leaders at all levels by giving them the resources to reward achievements of their people as and when they occur.
4. People are complex and largely driven by emotions. Building effective relationships increasingly requires understanding human behaviour. Leading "human centric" organizations increasingly invest in modern tools in this area.
5. People who are more aware of their own personality and behaviour can be more effective in their own personal development.
6. Developing internal resources to be part of change management is a powerful way of building credibility and integrity and building individuals own skills.
7. Treating people unfairly in the interests of saving money has a negative impact on culture and is a false economy.

Many organizations dismiss the "soft and fluffy" aspects of human behaviour and personality tools. This is a big mistake in todays people-centric business models. Sadly, most are unaware of the existing excess costs that are being incurred by not addressing underlying people issues. As Great Toys deploys its values, the importance of individual human behaviour is becoming apparent.

Fun Returns to Great Toys

10 Starting the changes

Now that there was agreement internally on all the "masthead" statements for the company - the purpose, the business model and the stakeholder values, the major push needed to be on rolling these commitments out. It had been agreed that Mina and Holly would develop the plan for communications down through the organization. Holly had also told Steve her plans for reviewing all the HR policies to bring them in line with the stated values; she had also taken on responsibility for supervisory and leadership development, as well as her continuing role to support operational needs such as Liz's hiring requirements. Steve thought that it was time for a health check with Holly, as he was starting to get concerned about her work load, and after the discussion with Liz it had become even more important.

That afternoon the regular management leadership meeting was scheduled, so Steve had arranged to meet Holly in the morning to check in with their progress. When she arrived at Steve's office she looked tired but seemed her usual positive self.

"So how are we doing Holly? I wanted to chat as I know you have a massive workload at the moment. How are you holding up?"

Holly smiled (as usual) and replied, "I have never been busier and the situation I have, reminds me of the phrase 'be careful what you ask for.' When I was hired I quickly began to realize what was needed here, but at the time my focus was mainly on developing policies and procedures around compliance issues. But I was getting frustrated, and just kept wishing someone would realize we had a strategic problem and needed to shift our focus. Then you came along, I got my wish and now I am going crazy!!"

"But are we on track? Do you need help in anything that we are doing?" Steve asked.

"I have all my staff working on bits of our projects so we can spread the work around. They are all really happy to be part of the change process that's going on - so in spite of the hard work and the hours, people seem to be enjoying it. I am also getting great support from the other managers, but I have some reservations that some people are not yet all fully on board."

"Help me understand that" Steve replied. "I thought we had the leadership team on side don't we? Do you see something that I don't?"

"Speaking frankly," Holly said, "there are two issues that I am concerned about. First, I am concerned about not having agreement with the board yet and that worries me although there is not much I can do about it."

Steve knew that he was delinquent in this situation; he was aware that he hadn't yet run things by the board although he believed that they had given him a tacit go ahead.

"You're right Holly - that's my problem. I don't think it will be an issue, but I do need to get on with it."

"Let me make a suggestion" Holly responded. "I think it would send a really powerful message if, once you talk to the board and make sure they agree, we then do two things. First, get the board to send out a personal message to every employee, telling them that they fully support this direction. That will build a lot of confidence. Second, and this is more for you to suggest to them, I think we need to raise the governance visibility of the culture issue, to be as important as a financial review. It should be something that you and I jointly report back to the board on every quarter as a minimum."

"I think those are great ideas Holly. Let me look after it. What is the other concern about senior managers?" Steve asked.

Holly hesitated for a moment. "This is a challenge Steve. I don't want to be in the position of suggesting that any one or other individual is not supportive of what we are doing - that would not be supportive of our leadership team - but my concern is that we don't know what their real feelings are about adopting these behaviours as the way we consistently do business. I think we need to - how do I put it, stress the team so that their real feelings come out. I think we need to find a way to find what emotional connection they have with the direction we are taking."

Steve then told Holly about the conversation with Sarah about the hidden qualities individuals had, and Holly confirmed she was aware of these approaches and had used them successfully in other organizations, mainly as an aid to hiring decisions. They agreed that Steve would raise this with the team at the next meeting.

Holly also raised some concerns about accountability and responsibility. She expressed some concern over clarity on Steve's expectation of her role in the culture change versus Mina's role. Who was in charge? How much authority did Holly have when she was working with Mina?

Steve explained that he thought Mina should take the lead role together with the culture change team on what he termed "the current project". Steve explained that he saw them as responsible for developing and communicating the roll out plans which both he and Holly would approve. He explained that he expected Holly to remain connected to a level that ensured the HR requirements needed to underpin the implementation of the culture change were being implemented. He clarified that as the responsible executive she had full authority to develop and make changes, but that all policy and procedure changes that would affect other departments should be run by the leadership team. It was agreed that she and Steve would formalize a bi-weekly update meeting with Mina to ensure there were no road blocks and key decisions which needed Steve's guidance could be taken.

Steve also asked Holly to start thinking about how Mina and the culture change team might transition to a more permanent role once the initial development and roll out was complete. "What I am thinking about," Steve explained, "is that we will need a continuing voice of the employee to make sure that any problems can be raised and dealt with – so that we don't slip back into our old ways. This might also be part of what we talked about relative to some sort of problem escalation process?" Holly agreed to give it some thought.

When they finished their discussion, Steve checked in with Judy about the board update.

"You must have ESP" Judy said as she smiled, "I just had a call from Simon from the board. He was hoping that we could schedule an extraordinary board meeting soon, as he has been talking with other board members and they have some thoughts and ideas that they want to run past you."

"Great" Steve replied, "the sooner the better. Look at my calendar and set something up for the board at a time that works for them all. Let Simon know that I want to give an update on our strategic direction at the same time - so maybe you and he can develop an agenda?"

Serendipity thought Steve. After lunch it was the weekly leadership team meeting. They had now started to develop an agenda so that they could stay on top of the key issues - both the operational recovery plans but also the major strategic initiatives. Judy was now taking notes at every meeting, which people were asked to review prior to the next meeting to ensure agreement.

Once the previous meeting notes were agreed and the first agenda items related to operational updates were completed, they moved on to the strategic issues. Mina and Holly had drafted a roll-out plan for communicating the purpose, business model and stakeholder statements. The suggestion was that it had to be a combination of communications and implementation steps. It was suggested that the "waves" would roll out as follows.

Phase 1 would focus on communications and initial feedback. This phase would involve a series of functional roll outs starting with each of Steve's direct reports who would then hold communication sessions with their staff and so on, to work its way through the functional frameworks. The goal would be to a) explain the role of the culture change team (that most people were already aware of either from the initial communications or personal involvement), and introduce how these documents were created, and b) obtain general feedback, and start some initial discussion on ideas to "make it real" through possible action items.

After this phase was complete there would be a review of the feedback by the culture change team together with the leadership team and, if required any modifications or interpretations would be developed.

Phase 2 would be a cross functional roll out using a "circles" concept. A number of groups drawn from volunteers from various departments would be created, and these would review the statements and discuss items that they saw as barriers to realizing the intent in operational reality. These groups would focus on the "real world operationalizing" of the changes needed to implement the commitments in the daily work of the business.

This would include developing ideas about how these statements could be developed with external stakeholders to strengthen Great Toys brand and reputation. A particular focus would be on suppliers and supply chain and on customers and the sales chain. These cross functional groups would develop recommendations and would seek approval from their respective managers and supervisors to work on their ideas.

Phase 3 would be a "how do we know" phase and would again use cross functional circles to develop ideas on what would be needed to sustain the desired behaviours and commitments in the longer term. This would include both ideas around reporting and feedback metrics and also on "people approaches" that would sustain and further develop areas such as trust, innovation, and creativity (and "having fun" was also mentioned!).

The leadership team had a few questions but generally felt this was a good practical approach. Two items were added. The first was the expansion of phase 2 to include functional circles of groups who would investigate the question of "what does this mean to me in my job." It was felt that people needed to ensure there was a clear connection between the organizational purpose and the expectation at the individual level of accountability and responsibility. It was suggested that maybe team or departmental statements could be developed to further define the expectations that could be used as part of training and orientation. Some people had expressed a concern that as the business grew a single corporate statement may not mean as much as something local. This has been reiterated by some people in the regional sales offices.

The second issue was an idea that once people had "internalized" what a commitment to the various statements actually meant in their own job, that each one would sign something like a "service pledge" to confirm their own personal "buy-in." This completed the discussion on the roll out.

The next key strategic issue that the two teams needed to address, had been raised some time ago and had not yet been followed up. This was the personal buy in by each of the leadership team members to the statements. The "self assessment" form that had been provided some time ago as the basis for a discussion was raised but the general feeling was that this was too bureaucratic and complicated, and that a better approach would be to focus on developing the leadership team themselves as "beacons" for "values based" leadership.

This was a good time for Steve to raise his upcoming meeting with the board to obtain final agreement to the three statements, (which he added he was fairly certain he would receive). He also provided his group with feedback on the individual "personality" assessment scheme that Sarah had suggested. There were several opinions and questions, but it was agreed that the leadership team would act as a pilot for the idea, so Steve agreed to contact the company and see when they could run a session. This raised a debate about workload; it was clear that everybody had their hands full with both their operational roles as well as the strategic shift initiatives. Adding team development on top of these seemed to be "the straw that was likely to break the camels back."

There was some discussion that included the need to develop guidelines on where the time was going to come from for all of these activities. It was agreed that all of the roll out and circle discussions would take place in work hours; it was felt this was important as it was the way they wanted to move forward in running the business, so they needed to assess the impact of making these approaches "part of the way we do things around here." This would be closely monitored to ensure that it was working.

Once that was dealt with, the conversation returned to how the leadership team itself would find time. Steve suggested that they had two options as he saw it, as he wanted to hold the session externally, to avoid interruptions. He suggested a one day retreat away from the office, which could either be on a workday or a weekend. It was an interesting discussion. What emerged was the potential of a negative signal being sent if all the staff were being asked to find time in their workday, but management went away to a resort or something.

Eventually it was decided that the best approach would be to hold it on company premises on a Saturday. Judy agreed to set it up. Based on Steve's initial investigation of the assessment process, he explained that each person would need to fill up a questionnaire prior to the meeting and that the results would then become part of what they discussed when they met. There were some concerns about whether personal information was going to be shared with the group to which Steve replied,

"Based on my discussions, that will be each persons' choice - however it was suggested that as the session develops each of you can make your own decision on how much you want to share."

This raised some quizzical responses, but the discussion eventually ended. Finally, Steve asked Holly to give the team an update on her work on aligning the HR framework to ensure all HR policies and procedures supported and reinforced the values. Holly explained the scope of the work and the way it was being undertaken. To help the team understand the level of detail they were looking at, Holly explained that they had developed an evaluation form that would be used now, to assess the level of alignment; this could then also be used in future policy development to ensure consistency.

Holly went on to explain that the approach that HR involved looking at each of the existing policies and procedures and assess their positive, negative, or absent correlation to the various values. Once this was completed they would have a priority list of the most critical "disconnects" which would be the first to be changed. She asked the others whether they could make their own staff aware of this process and look for suggestions of areas that should be investigated, as several people had already raised apparent inconsistencies.

Holly then showed an example of the assessment form that had been developed to assess each policy and procedure:

Score	Weight	Criteria
+ 3	Positive	There is a highly positive correlation and alignment between the organizations policy / procedure and the organizations stated values. Practicing this policy or procedure will reinforce the stated values and contribute toward credibility in our values.
+ 2		There is reinforcement of the organizations values and the policy / procedure is aligned but more could be done to improve the relationship
+ 1		There is a slight positive aspect to the policy or procedure relative to the organizations values but it does not strongly reinforce them
0	Neutral	Policy or procedure neither supports or reinforces the organizations values statements
-1	Negative	There is a slightly negative relationship between this policy / procedure and the organizations stated values; it will not have significant impact but should be corrected
-2		There is a disconnect between this policy / procedure and the organizations stated values and this should be corrected
-3		There is a strong and clear inconsistency between this stated policy / procedure and the stated values of the organization. Continuing to follow this approach will create inconsistency, negatively impact morale and demonstrate a lack of credibility between what we say and what we do.

Once the assessment form had been reviewed, Holly went on to pick up on Steve's discussion and the agreement that they would investigate the broader use of the personality assessment tool and explained one of the key reasons they were interested in this was to assist and support hiring decisions. As Holly explained,

"We already have a multiple interview process, including peer interviews. As you know this is progressively more challenging the more senior the role. We also have, for some positions, tests and standard questions that help us determine technical skills. What we don't have for almost any job, is anything other than the interview feedback and references that tell us about what behavioural principles come naturally to each person and what their "blind spots" may be in terms of how they interact with others. We think that this type of assessment will give us much greater insight into hiring decisions, promotions, and personal development plans. We also think that it will help develop and improve both internal and external working relationships."

"So, this would also be a key part of the leadership development for any one being considered for any supervisory position?" Charlene asked.

"Exactly," Holly responded. "You probably remember that one of the key issues the culture change team came up with was the criticality of the employee - supervisor relationship. They told us that the general feedback was that while the majority of managers were OK, there were a number that didn't seem to have the required leadership skills. The sooner we can identify this, the better our supervisory performance will be."

The conversation continued for a short time and the meeting ended. Again, Steve went around the table asking for feedback and a rating of both their "task" focus and their "relationship" focus. This time there was a bit more "opening up" and raising "tougher" issues that might otherwise have been buried or ignored. One person raised the issue of the amount of time they were putting into this "soft stuff." That person had rated task quite low and wondered why they couldn't just circulate the various documents for people to read, have them sign off on it and just deal with discipline when non-conformance occurred. They felt that this would save a lot of time and make them more productive. This generated some good discussion about how task and relationship must be balanced in practise, when so much focus is on performance and outcomes.

Steve apologized for getting on his soapbox again but asked the team to think about their time allocation in dealing with problems versus preventing problems.

"The challenge we have" he said "is that we intuitively know that Great Toys can perform at a better level. Yes, we can return to profitability by focusing on developing some new products and driving costs down, but the question always comes back to how much of our cost base is driven up, by areas like a lack of productivity, or an unwillingness to collaborate or share information. We see all the behavioural signs of the problems, but we don't know the costs."

Steve stood up and walked over to the flip chart and drew two lines with marks on them:

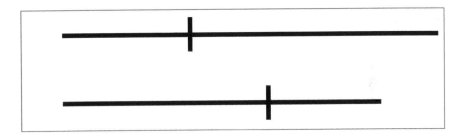

"What do you see?" Steve asked.

After a bit of laughter Liz said, "well not sure about anybody else but I see two lines with a mark on each one."

"But what else do you see?" Steve asked.

Liz replied, "well one line is longer than the other."

"Great. Exactly right," Steve confirmed, laughing, and adding that obviously they were all on form today. "Let me explain. Imagine each line represents the time it takes us to develop and get a product to market. The left hand end of each line is the design and development cycle, and the right half is the "operationalizing" of it. All the stuff Liz and her team have to do once the specifications are agreed. The top line is the way we do it today. We focus on functional accountability and responsibility. Each person does their job to meet their deadlines. Design - the left side, is completed on time, but poor Liz has a problem. When she and her team start to put things in place to make the product she starts to see problems. Liz has to get the design people back involved to do fixes and problem solving so that we can make whatever it is. That is what our cost base and our take to market reality is today."

Liz jumped in, and laughing said "how did you know about that Steve? This often happens and its not really anyone's fault its just that the practical reality of many things we have to think about are not considered."

"Exactly" Steve replied. "So, as you suggested Liz, the top line is longer than the bottom. Although we spend more time on design and development in the bottom line, the whole process is shorter because implementation goes more smoothly. That is called competitive advantage. If we spend more time on addressing possible issues and disagreement up front, implementation goes much more smoothly – even though out typical approach is to just get on with it."

Liz again spoke up "it's interesting to see that because in most advanced manufacturing businesses they learned this years ago and significantly improved their collaboration and cross functional team work to do exactly this - so it's not really a new idea."

"Agreed," Steve replied, "and the other thing is, that this applies everywhere to everything we do. The more collaboration and cooperation we have, the faster our overall cycle times will be - always assuming of course that our people are competent and have the tools and equipment that they need to do the job. Let me add one last thing. Consider change management. Do you think we are facing more or less change in the future?"

The team clearly agreed that change was a permanent reality of business today and Great Toys was a good example.

"Then think about the process of developing and implementing changes to anything we do - products, services, internal processes, external relationships and on and on. The more effectively we can work together, the shorter the cycle time for change management. If we can do things faster and more effectively than the competition, then that is a major competitive advantage."

"So, the message is that we all have to have some level of faith in what we are doing. We have to believe that the changes we are making is getting us to a new way to run the business – even though it is frustrating at times. We are spending more time on relationships because all the research tells us that organizations who score high in their employee relationships also score high on performance. Relationship building is the enabler of performance. In the past we focused mainly on task but that needs to change. Task remains important but the relationships that 'enable' task, are of equal importance."

There were some smiles and a smattering of applause; Steve took a bow.

"Well, I did tell you it was a soapbox" he responded.

"It's interesting," Holly observed, "that sometimes in business we have to do what we think is right. The numbers alone may not show it, but if you think back to where we all started this, we agreed we needed to take a systems view of our business model. I think we can see from the work the culture change team has done, that there are some gaps. While there may not be clear cause and effect we know there is a correlation. I am certainly happy with where we are headed."

Once again the meeting had been long, but they felt that they had accomplished a lot. While some members appeared to be "opening up" a little more, there was clearly some way to go yet in making sure everyone was "on board."

When Steve went back to his office, he and Judy reviewed the following weeks schedule and then they both headed out for the weekend. Steve was looking forward to another two days of rest and relaxation back at home and was also hoping that they might be able to think some more about their own family plans which needed to be clarified before the school year was completed.

THOUGHTS AND IDEAS

1. Motivated employees can become so committed that they create their own health problems. Leaders should look out for this – care about "the person." (Steve / Holly concerns).
2. People will also worry if they see "holes in the plan." Holly is right to express her concerns to Steve about the board.
3. Having the board publicly support Steve and the culture change team would be a powerful vote of confidence.
4. Readers may by this time be concerned about "lack of implementation", but the activities of the culture change team are already part of the transition. The line between plan and implement is not always clear – and is often iterative.
5. The "push back" on leadership team development is normal. Thinking that "task" outweighs "values / behaviour." They are inter-dependent and "short changing" the people side would be a false saving.
6. Applying the "total elapsed time" concept to a people-centric organization is valid but often overlooked. Planning the human dimension is equally important to process planning.

Again, in this chapter we see Steve acting as a coach but also being open to his own self development by raising concerns with others and asking for their advice and input.

11 Catching up

Steve had an enjoyable weekend with his family; their plans for Steve's permanent move as CEO were discussed again, and the general decision was that they would stay in their house in the city but would look for an upgrade to the place in Two Rivers that would accommodate the whole family. This was so they would maintain flexibility while the children finished school, and once that happened they would decide on whether to sell the city house and move permanently or take some other course of action.

Steve was able to spend some quiet time with Jenny talking over the progress at Great Toys. Steve's level of stress had remained in control as he was gradually seeing the changes he felt were needed, start to fall into place. He talked about the personal reservations and concerns that he still had, which he had not discussed with others at work, about whether the changes being made would in fact deliver a noticeable difference. This ability to doubt himself was not new to Steve - in fact it was a quality that Jenny had come to know well. They talked about the "speech" that he made on Friday afternoon at the leadership team meeting - his soapbox as he called it, as he tried to "rally the troops" to believing in where they were headed.

"That's an important role you play" Jenny said. "Leadership comes in all sorts and types, but you were exercising inspirational leadership at that point. This is the 'I have a dream' type of sharing. I am sure many of them have some level of misgivings. A lot of their careers have probably been spent in traditional command and control type organizations, that often pay lip service to people issues but never really change the way they do things to engage, share and trust employees. For some it's a big step. They need your encouragement."

"Yes I know" Steve responded, "but every so often my imposter syndrome takes over."

Jenny laughed "Oh yes, you talk a good talk but underneath you are quaking in your shoes and fearing that someone will discover you really have no idea what you are doing, and you will be called out and ridiculed for your lack of integrity and experience."

They both laughed. "Yes I know its just my mind playing tricks on me - but when I am leading a team into new territory, I do sometimes worry that I may not be right."

"That's leadership" Jenny replied, "as long as you do as much research as possible and assess the upside and downside risks of the decisions that you take, then you just have to go with it."

"I guess so" Steve responded, "but I know part of my own personality is that I like to do the research and have all the numbers to support my decisions. It seems the higher your role in the organization, the harder it is to do that. I am well aware of analysis-paralysis and try to guard against, but in so many of these situations when I have to look at the business as a system, I have to rely on more subjective indicators and trends in making total business model or system decisions. Its' almost like we don't have an adequate level of objective information or metrics that provide a good basis for decisions."

"Hm" Jenny said as she considered this. "An interesting observation. I think that is why much of the developing research on leadership is starting to tell us that there is no single quality that makes a great leader, but the ability to have a broad base of awareness that can call on several qualities and balance these in the same way that an effective organization needs to be balanced to operate effectively. It also reinforces the importance of the values because these provide a foundation of moral thinking you can fall back on. You may not know the facts, but is it the right, fair and ethical thing to do?"

"That makes sense" Steve replied, "there doesn't seem to be much learning or guidance out there that teaches CEO's how to operate an integrated business, that balances performance and sustainability – especially in today's human-centric businesses. You can never make everybody happy but what steps do you need to take to optimize performance?"

"One place to start is by looking at your own natural abilities[v]" Jenny responded. " We talked just now about inspirational leadership which is one quality that leaders call up when needed; but any leader also needs at some point the ability to work through people and work with the numbers and at some point to push for results. These are all qualities that effective leaders have in varying degrees. A great leader is someone who is aware of these different aspects, calls upon them when needed and gets help in aspects they are not as well developed in."

"What do you think about my pay?" Steve suddenly asked.

Jenny laughed, "that's a quick change of direction. Well, as long as it is enough to keep me in the style I have become accustomed to that is fine" she replied, laughing.

"Seriously," Steve continued, "the reason I ask is that I am well aware that in the absence of actual information, people make guesses that impact their attitudes." (He then told Jenny about the outburst at the culture change meeting and how someone told him he didn't understand because he lived in a different world). Steve continued:

"From some of the feedback we received from the culture change team, I get the impression that some employees think I am raking it in. Being a private company, we don't disclose that. What do you think? Should we? I know that in the mind of the general public there is a feeling of unfairness and inequity based on what they hear about CEO pay and it can obviously be a source of perceived unfairness."

"I honestly don't know Steve" Jenny replied thoughtfully. "I don't actually know how your pay compares to other people, but I admit I would err on the side of disclosure. I know that CEO compensation has gone from about twenty times employees average pay in the 1950's to ridiculous numbers now, so it is a key irritant for employees and certainly contributes to their feeling of unfairness. I think you should talk to the board about it - after all they are the ones' who really call the shots in that area, right?"

Steve reflected that it was great to have Jenny to talk with. Someone who through the years had come to know him more deeply than anyone else - even his parents who knew him from his earlier years yet often didn't really know or understand some of his qualities as an adult. He couldn't help thinking if that level of mutual knowledge and understanding existed within the workplace, it would give a powerful advantage to developing honesty and trust. They both decided that was enough business talk -and moved on to relaxing with a glass of wine.

When Steve arrived at the office on Monday morning, Judy told him that the board would be able to meet with him on Wednesday, and that the facilitator for the team session was also available next Saturday. Steve asked Judy to check with the others involved, confirm both items, and to ensure that the questionnaires for the assessments were distributed as soon as possible. Judy also told him that the facilitator suggested that she and Steve meet before Saturday to go over the process as well as allowing her to understand a bit more about the people who would be there and the business of Great Toys. Steve confirmed that they should meet face to face, and asked Judy to fit it into his calendar.

His first meeting was with John in marketing to talk about feedback of the trade show and their progress on social media. It seemed from their discussion, that things had gone well.

"The order intake was at least twenty percent above what we expected which will put our potential revenues higher than Tony had in the projections. The other great thing was that we did receive orders from two customers that we had lost, that had originally been with us for a long time. They were really positive when I met them at the show and were asking all sorts of questions about what we were doing. I mentioned the social media posts that we were making and again they found that very helpful and wanted to see more regular updates from us."

"That is great news, John" Steve replied. "It was unfortunate that I could only be at the show for a short time during the opening."

"Yes, it would have helped if you had been there the whole time - but given our situation, I don't think that would have been realistic; but that's not all" John continued. "The toys that we jointly developed with the suppliers with the new materials that are targeted at environmentally aware parents went down really well and attracted a new group of clients that we have not seen before. There was also a lot of interest in our overall approach to new product development, both with the community pipeline but also with our efforts to engage both suppliers and customers with market focused development."

"Seems like a strategic initiative we should grow then?" Steve asked. "Have you talked to Charlene or any of the others about this?"

"Yes, in fact we had an informal feedback session after the show with a lot of the key people who were involved with the rapid development and ramp up" John explained. "They were all so invested in the whole effort that they all felt that they somehow owned the success and wanted to know all about it. I think in the future the trade shows may be a great place for more of our team to participate in - it really gives you great exposure."

"So, what was their feedback?" Steve asked.

"The main thing was that Charlene had the opportunity to tell us about her ideas for 'Partners in Play' that she had discussed with you - and the groups feeling was that this could be a great branding opportunity to position ourselves as a central point within a toy evolution ecosystem."

"Is that something you want to run with as a group then" Steve asked.

"Absolutely" John replied. "We decided that if you agreed, this would be an opportunity to jointly develop a specific strategic initiative to roll out as a foundation for future growth. All we need from you, apart from your blessing, is some core goals that we need to aim for, and we will do the rest."

"I think the core goals are already there" Steve smiled. "We have all agreed on our purpose statement, and we know we need to grow the business and develop market focused products to survive - remember the business model where we laid out our commitment to customers, suppliers, community, and others? As long as it supports those aims I think the team should blast forward. I am sure as you develop the plan you will need financial resources - but when you get to that stage, you can work with Tony so we can look at the ROI and make sure your plan is layered in as a core strategic growth initiative."

"Fantastic" John responded. "Now I think you also wanted an update on social media. A number of key issues. First, the core use of existing public platforms like Facebook, TikTok and others are all up and running. We have a company page on all the sites that we can, and these are being monitored in real time. By the way, Sarah's daughter Heather has been incredibly helpful in making this happen; she was so excited by what we are doing that she has been helping start to develop our longer term plans."

"Sounds good - where do we go from here then? I gather we have bought ourselves some time, but I assume there are farther reaching issues?" Steve asked.

"Yes. Strategically we have a growing challenge and to a degree it ties in with the discussions and activities we have been having on culture change. But let me ask you question - do you consider me accountable and responsible for our branding, image, and reputation?" John asked.

"Absolutely" Steve responded. "That is a core aspect of your responsibility."

"Then in today's reality I have to tell you that I can't do the job" John replied smiling. Steve's eyebrows shot up and he was clearly stunned, but John continued.

"Don't get me wrong. I can and will do the job but in the reality of todays business, I cannot do it as a functional responsibility alone. There are just too many interconnections and technology at the heart of it. What we need at Great Toys is a cross functional circle or council or something, that we task with being the custodians of the corporate image. I would like to move ahead on that basis and develop a small team of people who would still be in their traditional functional departments."

"From what I see and hear I think that is the way to go" Steve responded. "But there has to be more to it than that?"

"Yes and that is part of the problem" John continued. "First, effective collection and analysis of core business data is at the heart of strategic business decision making. We are collecting data but there is no one actively involved in our business at the leadership team level, who can understand the business and how data, information and broad based knowledge can be brought together to help us make better, more informed, and faster decisions at the total Great Toys level."

"Sounds like a pitch for a position upgrading or a Director of IT?" Steve replied.

"Sort of" John continued, "but I think what we really need is a bit different. I think we need, what could we call it? A director of integrated knowledge maybe? The key is that we need someone who understands IT at the technical level but whose contribution is in bringing knowledge of all sorts and sources together to support our thinking and decision making."

"Well, it sounds reasonable, and I have a bias towards thinking you are correct - but it will be expensive I am sure, and we don't have the budget at the moment anyway" Steve replied.

John laughed and replied, "yes I know money is always a scarce resource, but I will keep pushing the product side to give you the revenues so we can plan to re-invest a bit of it for this purpose."

It was Steve's turn to laugh "OK, that's fair. Look, I am generally in agreement. Can you work with Tony and Holly to develop the idea and then we need to run it by the whole team as it's a key decision in both how we run the business moving forward but also a key resource allocation. Some of them will want input on that."

This discussion reminded Steve that when he had met Simon for the board discussion, they had also talked about his successful career in IT. He seemed very aware of what was happening in IT and might also be a great resource. Steve tucked the idea away for later.

"The other key things that make this an imperative" John explained, "is that while the website and the on-line order entry system are working OK now, they really must be integrated with our social media activity. We need a seamless technology solution, and we need someone to look after it. More importantly, and I don't want to scare you Steve as its' a bit down the road but there is the metaverse."

"Come again" Steve replied, "the meta what?"

"The metaverse" John repeated. "Are you familiar with virtual reality? Its often used now in things like computer gaming." Steve nodded. "The metaverse is what people are seeing as the evolution of technology and the merging of areas like on-line shopping and virtual reality. Down the road people will be able to visit a Great Toys virtual store, walk around, look at toys, talk to shop assistants and get advice and then order things. This will all be computer based, and with the upcoming generation, my thinking is that this is where we need to be headed."

"Surely this is way out?" Steve asked.

"Maybe - but it has started already" replied John. "Although there are some signs of it picking up slower than expected, some companies are already paying for advertising within systems being developed. I am not suggesting we become a leading edge first adopter, but as we move forward we need to know where our buying public is headed and building our capability to serve that market with our business model."

"Amazing" Steve sighed, "I guess we find ourselves on a bit of a treadmill! I really appreciate your strategic thinking on this John. I am really happy you are on top of where things are going. I think this would be a core issue for the cross functional group that you suggest looking after brand and image. We need to figure out when will this happen? How? What systems and processes will it impact? How will we organize our business model to respond? Those are all critical issues that the circle or council or whatever we call them should address."

"Let me talk with Tony and Holly and we will look at the shorter term IT decisions" John replied. "I will also develop the idea for the brand custodians and will bring that back to the leadership team for discussion within a couple of weeks."

With that, they wrapped up the meeting. Steve felt really positive. Already people were starting to take responsibility and accountability, promote cross functional collaboration and thinking and developing ideas about how Great Toys could grow and succeed in the future.

Steve had not talked to Gord for some time. Gord had been the director of sales when Steve arrived, but his wife had been taken seriously ill. Steve and he had mutually agreed that he would give up the sales role for a leave of absence and they would decide later what role he would take when he returned. They had agreed to have lunch to catch up and see how things were going.

When Steve arrived at the restaurant, Gord was already there and rose as Steve approached the table.

"It is so great to see you Steve" Gord started, "and again thank you for allowing me this time away from the business. How are things going?"

"Well, I must admit you look good Gord. I think it is important that you have this time - I think it was for the best. Things, as you say, are going well. We started a rapid response program for some new products for the upcoming season and those have done well. We are finally seeing an uptick in order generation. We are also moving ahead on some of the culture changes. So, to answer your question, it is busy but hopefully headed in the right direction. But how about you?"

"That's good news about the business, Steve. For me it's what we expected. My wife Angie has continued her downward slide and has now been moved to palliative care, as there is not much that can be done at this stage. She has lost a lot of her motor skills and has trouble communicating. It's really sad. The kids have been great support, but they have their own lives to live. The doctors tell me it's a matter of just a few weeks at the most now. So, we just battle on - but I am really appreciative that I have been able to have this time with her."

"I'm so sorry" Steve responded, "although I know words can't be a lot of consolation. Just know that when you are ready we can chat about what you want to do - but there is no hurry."

They worked their way through lunch with lots of small talk and reminiscences about the business. It was good to get Gord's thoughts and inputs on the way things used to be, but it was also clear that the spark was not there any more.

"I have to tell you Steve, I am really not sure whether I will want to come back. After all this, maybe I should spend more time with the grand-children and do some travelling. Anyway, I have put it all in the back of my mind for the moment, and when the time comes we can chat."

They eventually parted company and Steve had a feeling that the next thing they would hear would be the passing of Angie. Gord had served the company well and Steve would make sure he was treated right whatever he decided.

Steve spent the rest of the day catching up on reports and action items that needed to be taken care of. Judy had arranged for the team facilitator to come in the next day.

The next day arrived, and Janet Parvane introduced herself and the company called Collective Minds[vi]. It turned out that Janet had been involved with Collective Minds since its inception and was a part owner of the business with a strong background in both business but also sociology.

She explained that she often acted as a facilitator for new clients, and also that she knew Sarah well.

"Interesting background" asked Steve, "I would have thought psychology not sociology" he asked.

Janet laughed "that often comes up" she said, "sociology was what I ended up studying in my undergrad, but it is more relevant, as it is about the issues of people relationships, rather than an in-depth understanding of the technical and medical aspects."

She went on to explain to Steve how the whole process worked. Participants would fill up an on-line personal questionnaire that would then be processed and a personal report for each person would be produced. While the basic report described an individuals overall natural tendencies, the more advanced version that they would be using, provided an understanding of three different aspects called "qualities" of an individual. Theses were underlying, everyday and over-extended.

Janet continued and explained that "everyday persona" reflects how most people see you, whereas the "underlying persona" is your natural person; the "over-extended persona" reflects how an individuals qualities change when they are put under stress.

"Knowing this information" Janet explained, "should help in a number of ways. The thing we will focus on initially is communications as that is an important aspect of building relationships that lead to effective cooperation and collaboration. Later on, we can look at several other aspects in more depth, but our first session is really designed for participants to see how the process works and what information it provides."

"So, what do we achieve in this first session?" Steve asked. "Will we need follow on sessions, or how does that work?"

Janet explained, "the goal of this first session on Saturday will firstly be to explain the whole concept of personal qualities and tendencies. After that is completed, we use a set of cards with individual personality traits on each card, and we do an exercise where people keep the cards that they think apply to themselves and give away the one's that don't to other people on the team, where they think the description applied more to them. It's usually a fun exercise and it prepares people to look at their own detailed reports."

"That sound good," Steve replied – "what happens next?"

"Then we hand out each individual's personal report," Janet continued to explain. "Once people have looked at their own reports, they get to provide feedback on how accurate they think the information being provided is, considering the cards that they felt fitted them, plus the cards that others had passed on to them. Hopefully this builds credibility in the process. Then we do a communications exercise and at that point people have the choice as to whether to share their information with others or keep it private."

"OK, but given the personal nature of this activity, are there risks?" Steve asked.

Janet continued, "in our experience there will be some level of scepticism at first, but we usually find that once people look through their reports and compare them to the feedback form the cards that they and their peers have ended up with, that drops significantly, as long as they are honest. It's my job to manage that process for you - but what it will tell you is whether you are going to have one or more people on your team that not only have behavioural blind-spots but may also be resistant to personal feedback and reflection. Sometimes these people may be known for having over-developed ego's and possibly be highly narcissistic which can be a problem as your team development moves forward."

"I think I understand - can you just help me make sure I know what this means?" Steve asked.

"Well technically, at its' worst, it is considered a personality disorder," Janet replied. "It is a mental condition in which people have an inflated sense of their own importance, a deep need for excessive attention and admiration, troubled relationships, and a lack of empathy for others. Those are my technical words, but in terms of being part of a fully functioning inter-dependent leadership team, they spell problems."

"I don't think we have anybody in that situation" Steve replied, "but it will be interesting to see."

Janet showed Steve examples of the reports and explained how they would proceed. After that, she asked Steve to provide an overview of Great Toys including its history and where they were now, in terms of what they were trying to achieve. Janet seemed quite familiar with many of the challenges that Steve described. Finally, she asked for a quick description or bio on each of the people who would be at the session on Saturday; Janet told Steve that she would look through all the reports once the data had been collected, but she also needed his perspective before she did that.

Steve mentioned that Judy would be there at the Saturday session but was not really a part of the leadership team - an observation that Janet corrected.

"I don't think you can say Judy is not part of the team if she is there - she should be able to fully participate. Also, if her function is to support you in your role as CEO and interact with people on your behalf then she really needs to understand you and the others as well as herself. I think she should be included."

Steve nodded in agreement. They called Judy in at that point to let her know that she was included in the whole exercise. Janet showed Judy how to sign in to the Collective Minds on-line system, and helped her set up the names of the participants and send out a standard letter to each one with a web-link to the site where the questionnaires could be completed.

After some more conversation Janet left, telling Steve that if anything came up, he could call her, otherwise she would see them on Saturday. Steve decided that he would fill his responses up after he had left work.

THOUGHTS AND IDEAS

1. Inspirational leadership is one of several "qualities" effective leaders call upon from their behavioural toolbox.
2. Steve is right to think about what message executive compensation gives others about perceived fairness.
3. For the company, being back visibly at the trade show leverages the internal changes – new ideas, partnerships, commitment to social activity and environment. Constant market opinion and feedback should be a core driver of strategy.
4. We start to see how a company purpose and shared values, especially with stakeholders provides a foundation for people to "get on with it."
5. The new marketing VP, John, starts to clearly demonstrate the cross functional collaboration needed to optimize a business model. The council for brand image and reputation is an great example.
6. Steve still has to find time to support Gord.
7. Real-time feedback on employees attitudes and engagement is key – to assess changes as they move forward.

Steve continues to juggle many things that are successfully moving forward – but again it's a journey of exploration. One needs to be open to new ways of approaching leadership and management. As Sarah said long ago – people can be hard to lead.

12 Is the board with us?

The next morning Steve was scheduled to meet with the board to hear the feedback from ideas that Simon had been working on, as well as to update them on his own work around the values and their strategic direction.

Steve had asked Simon if he could just give an informal update at the beginning; he hoped that he could establish a positive climate if he confirmed that they were on-track with the quarterly projections and that the new product launch had been a success.

It seemed to work. The board members listened intently and asked several questions but seemed pleased and relieved that the first steps in the recovery plan were well under way and actually delivering results.

"We still have a long way to go" Steve concluded, "but at least I think this begins to demonstrate that we can stabilize things and build the base needed for recovery."

Simon then took over and gave a recap starting with the earlier board meeting, where he pointed out that Steve had been given a bit of a rough ride. He then talked about the importance of the board in providing both oversight but also support and advice to Steve, and Steve's own initiative of working with Sarah as well as approaching Simon to seek a more lasting solution to his need for the board to provide advice. He also reminded the board that Steve's father had previously been Chairman of the Board, but that role had been combined with the CEO role. He finished up by summarizing some of the "good governance" guidelines released by the FRC[vii] as guidance for public companies and pointed out that these suggest the separation of the role of Chair and the CEO. He then turned to Steve.

"Since you chatted with me Steve, I have been talking with the current members of the board about the possibility of changes. I pointed out that you wanted a much closer relationship with the board, especially in an advisory role, so were looking for expertise. You had also indicated that business was changing at a fast pace, and that because of this, it would be helpful to have additional people on our board, who were knowledgeable in some of these changes." Simon looked around the table and confirmed that all the heads were nodding in agreement.

Simon continued "I also took the liberty of circulating the good governance guidelines to the board members and we agree that your request is timely, and it would help us renew the board and more closely reflect the current expectations. So here is what we are recommending - although you haven't actively taken the Chair role, we wanted to run these past you, then we can discuss it and hopefully agree."

Simon then laid out the following plan, and suggested that if agreed, he would work with the other board members to move ahead and implement the changes.

Firstly, it was agreed that an updated board charter would be developed, to deal with leadership, including the role of Chair, division of responsibilities, approaches to composition, succession and evaluation, the boards role in risk management, audits, and board evaluation and finally board composition. They agreed to generally try and model their own charter on the good governance guidelines.

Next, the board would be a minimum of five and maximum of eight people including a Chair who could not be the CEO but had to be a non-executive member.

There would be a recruitment and nomination committee, composed of the Chair and one board member, and they would also introduce board rotation of external (non-family) members. External board members would serve for a specified term between three and five years.

To start these changes, it was agreed that Jim Carlisle, who had been on the board for over twenty years, would retire. (Simon publicly thanked him for his service as did the rest of the board). Two new directors were being recommended who had already been interviewed by Simon and Francis (Eccles, the wife of the previous CEO). All that remained was for Steve to interview them to make sure he was happy.

Assuming these changes went ahead, this would bring the board complement to five including Steve and Francis as family members, Simon who would continue, plus the two new directors.

There was a minimum amount of discussion. Steve asked if the new candidates had backgrounds that would add to the boards ability to provide advice and support and there were a few smiles.

"Oh, I think so Steve," Simon replied, "and I don't see any reason not to tell you who we are proposing as you have already met one of them."

Steve looked surprised, "now you really have my interest."

"The first suggestion is Sarah Brightside. We know she has been working with you and when we approached her she was excited to have her involvement raised a notch. We think Sarah will bring broad based business acumen as well as an understanding of the changes you are making, and she will make a great board member. The second person is James Lee-Chin; you don't know him, but he has a strong legal background, runs a number of businesses and is very progressive in the area of people management. We think he would be ideal."

Steve smiled and replied, "well obviously I am really happy about Sarah joining, so as far as she is concerned I think you can just move ahead. I look forward to meeting James and I am sure he will be equally acceptable. Thanks for this Simon, and the rest of you. I think these suggestions are a really positive move to bring the board and management closer together."

There was also some discussion about future expansion of the board, and it was agreed that as the company grew and expanded, it would become clearer what additional skills were needed at the board level and the decision would be made at that time. Simon had apparently also explained to the board that a much wider set of options including employee representation might be considered in the future.

At that point the floor was handed over the Steve. They agreed that while the new directors should be part of approving the strategic direction Steve was taking, confirming his direction could not wait, so they needed to move ahead.

Judy had circulated the three statements that management and the culture change team had agreed prior to the meeting, so no time was lost in reading them through, but Steve did provide the background to the original creation of the culture change team, and the work that they had done in collecting information and identifying the gaps between their suggested and desired behaviours and the current situation.

There were a number of probing questions about the statement. The purpose statement was not an issue, but as they moved into the business model and then the stakeholder values there was concern over the amount of detail and the commitments that were being made. While it put a lot of pressure on Steve to justify what he was presenting, the input was generally constructive although concerned.

He was asked about legal liability inherent in making these types of commitments and agreed that although he didn't believe it was an issue, he would check them out with legal counsel. Steve pointed out that part of the challenge was that many of the expectations that were being put forward were there to cover areas either not clarified by legal requirements or those that were generally understood to be ethical in nature. This raised concern over committing to things that would eventually add to their financial demands, that might make them non-competitive - especially if they were doing things over and above minimum legal requirements. This was a particular interest in the statement "zero harm to the natural environment."

"Yes, you may be correct" Steve responded, "but if it is the right thing to do and it is a growing expectation from our stakeholders as well as society in general, I believe that we should exhibit leadership and do what's right. If we don't do it, the impact may be on a loss in customers or difficulty in attracting key talent, and probably a decline in our brand and reputation. I don't think we can take that risk."

One item was discussed that sent Steve back to do some more work. "I see you have a statement about being ethical in your stakeholder values" Francis asked. "What exactly do you mean by that?"

"Like we talked about relative to no harm to the natural environment," Steve responded. "It is about working within the law but going further and operating in a way that meets the expectations of society - even if no laws cover the situation."

"Are you sure your people will understand that" Francis replied? "If you made a general statement like that, I still think people might be confused. Ethics is a really hard area, and many things are not black and white but grey. Many organizations provide general guidelines and put a system in place to obtain management advice and direction when a question comes up. Is that what you plan, because if so, that seems just to add more bureaucracy to me."

"What are you suggesting then?" Steve asked.

Francis replied, "I don't think you can have a general statement without some sort of underlying guidance. You haven't mentioned it and I don't see it, but I think you need a code of ethics that people sign, which provides some level of assurance that everyone understands and commits. In many countries this is now a mandatory requirement as part of risk management and internal controls."

There was general agreement around the table that this was an added step that Steve should take. Steve thought they were finished once there were no more questions, but then Simon spoke up.

"This is great Steve, and we can all support it with the changes we have suggested, but there is a whole other area that we haven't talked about, and as far as I am concerned if we don't deal with it, this whole discussion has been a waste of time."

Steve was tired and starting to get frustrated, especially as he thought Simon was an ally. Now he was throwing a spanner in the works. There had also been a few "body language" indications from other board members that seemed to suggest "oh dear, what now, I thought we were done."

"I am not sure what we missed - what are you concerned about?" Steve asked.

"Mainly about our ability to support implementation and sustainability of these commitments. As a board we will need two things. First, we need some feedback including metrics that provide us with some assurance that these initiatives are sustaining a high level of employee engagement and strong relationships between your key stakeholders.

Second, we need to add to the regular quarterly updates which mainly covers financials at the moment, a review of the whole ESG performance including an emphasis on the people situation. We need feedback on climate change initiatives that cover the whole environment area. We need feedback as I said on the whole challenge of people issues, and lastly we need feedback on societal issues. Not just ethical aspects but activities related to our responsibility to the community and beyond. We can work out the details but that is what's missing."

Steve breathed a sigh of relief and replied "you had me worried for a bit Simon, but I agree 100%. As you can say we can work out the details, but I can tell you this has already come up internally as an issue we have to develop, and the board's needs are clearly an extension of that discussion."

The meeting had taken the whole morning - a little longer than planned but the good news was that the board was supportive. As a last request, Steve asked if the board would be willing to sign off on their agreement and write a note to all employees, showing their support and expectations. This, together with the inclusion of the culture change aspects on future board agendas, would align the work that was happening internally closely to the board oversight and governance responsibility.

The board agreed, so Steve could move ahead. It was agreed that Judy would draft a support statement and circulate it to the board members to obtain agreement prior to sending it out. It was agreed this was now a high priority.

They were about to wrap up when Francis asked for a few minutes. While people clearly wanted to leave, they all sat back down.

"First, as you all know this has been a hard transition for me" she explained. "The loss of Bob was tragic for both the business and clearly, for personal reasons. I was not feeling positive about the business after Bob's death, as to a degree I felt it was his work that was creating a growing level of stress. I am sure that none of you are aware that it was essentially 'doctors orders' that resulted us taking the vacation during which he passed."

There were several head shakes and murmurs of condolence as Francis continued. "But life must move forward. I had some strong reservations about Steve taking over, but it was clearly the best choice for the family. I knew the stress that the work had placed on Bob and was fearful it would be more of the same once you took over Steve. But your commitment, enthusiasm and desire for change had not only convinced me that the future can now be brighter, but that you are doing a great job for us as a family and that the business is in good hands."

Steve was a little embarrassed by this display of support, especially when some of the others clapped Francis statement.

Francis went on "so again, thank you Steve for coming back and taking this on. I also want to express the family's support again for Jim's time spent on the board. I would like to present you, as a gift from the family with this cheque together with a commitment to pay for a fully funded and complementary holiday for you and your wife to anywhere in the world that you desire. We know you wanted to travel and here is your chance."

Sarah handed over the gifts amid applause from the others in the room. Jim had tears in his eyes and made a short speech thanking the board and the family for the honour in serving. With that and fond farewells, the meeting finally broke up and Steve returned to the office.

Later that afternoon, Steve got a call from Tony who told him that he, Liz, and Josh needed to talk to Steve urgently. His initial reaction was "what now," but he agreed, and they arrived a short time later.

"We have a big problem with some of the new toys" Josh stated. "We need some guidance from you Steve as money will be involved and it will add some stress to our already busy schedules."

"I dread to ask" Steve replied. "What's happened now?"

"Well, it's great news really but does create a potential problem," Tony responded.

"Get to the point" Steve asked, clearly concerned.

Josh replied, "as you know the new toys have done well at the trade show, and we have been working 110% to get the orders out, but it appears one of our key competitors, who had broken into one of our originally loyal customer accounts, is not having such a good time. Apparently they are having trouble meeting deliveries because of glitches in their supply chain - a lot of their products come from China."

"OK, that sounds promising" Steve replied, " but again how does it impact us?"

"They were at the trade show and came to visit and liked what they saw. But they told us at the time that they were already committed this season but might come back to us in the future, Now, they have come back with an emergency request for us to step in and supply our products to fill their gaps."

"Fantastic" Steve exclaimed "I am sure that's why Liz is here right. What do you think Liz, can we do it?"

"Yes," Liz replied, "but that is also why Tony is here. My problem is that I will need to incur some significant extra costs to enable us to meet the requirements in time, but if we can get over that hurdle we can do it."

"Tony?" Steve asked, looking at him for guidance.

"Yes, I can look after the funding, but the challenge will be that our margins will decline, even though we will still make a small profit on the order."

"So, we can do the right thing, gain a returning customer, increase our revenues, put more cash in the bank, but our margins will drop? Not sure I see the issue?" Steve responded.

They laughed and Tony replied "that's why I am the accountant and you run the business. The issue will be that the bank in particular may look at a lower than expected margin percentage as a problem - but I am sure they will see the benefits if we explain the reasons."

"Could we go back to this client and tell them we have to increase our prices because of the late orders?" Steve asked.

Josh replied, "yes we could Steve, and Tony had already suggested that. My concern is that it will send the wrong message. We will clearly be taking advantage of the situation. If we think back to our values, I prefer that we focus on building the relationship, by clearly showing that we are doing them a favour, rather than just focusing on making money on this single transaction."

"Interesting" replied Steve. "So, you re looking at this favour as a sort of investment in the relationship that will create future ROI?"

"Exactly. If we think about customers as partners that we invest in developing, then we will value the relationship rather than trying to just make quote by quote, order by order decisions. The fact that they came back to us demonstrates not just loyalty but faith in our ability. I believe if we do this we will have a very appreciative customer who will also value the relationship - although I am sure they will still expect us to be competitive. Even better they will tell other people that we helped them out"

"Let's do it," Steve replied. "To me this is a great strategic decision that allows us to trade off customer capital and financial capital. Thanks to all of you. Great idea. Good decision. Just make sure the customer knows and appreciates what we are doing for them, including telling them we will be absorbing some extra costs."

"Oh, I plan to" Josh replied, laughing. "They will be reminded about this for some time!"

THOUGHTS AND IDEAS

1. Steve is working with a board member to start the changes needed. Steve needs a "champion" for change at the board level and he seems to have found one.
2. Note how the board does not micro-manage but asks key probing questions. This is their role. Steve should be ready.
3. The board also plays its' role well in asking for accountability so they can measure progress.
4. Notice the linkage to ESG – with the board changes addressing the "G," while the human, employee and social aspects address the "S". The "E" is also clearly embedded.
5. Notice how people are "coming around" to Steve's direction once they understand.
6. Also notice the valuable advice related to developing a code of ethics. Also see it comes from someone that may have deemed a "personal problem" for him based on history.
7. See how both John and Tony are using their "freedom to express opinions" and how this leads to positive outcomes.
8. Also note the importance on not taking advantage of a situation. Win / win rather than win / lose. The basis of relationship building.

Many initiatives are now moving ahead and delivering results. If leaders support and encourage this, it will act as positive reinforcement that Steve and the team are serious about the change and committed to seeing it through.

---

13 Do I really know you?

Later that week, Simon and Judy had arranged for Steve to meet with James Lee-Chin the person who was being recommended for the board. Although Steve did not react when they arrived at his office, it was clearly a surprise. Simon introduced James, and fortunately he broke the ice when he started to introduce himself.

"Yes," James said, "I will be your visible minority on the board," and with that they all laughed. He went on the explain his career and experience focusing on the value he felt this experience would bring to the board. He explained how he had originally been born in Kenya, with an Indian father and a local mother; he also added that he felt that his appointment to, and presence on the board would provide additional reinforcement to the commitment of Great Toys to diversity and inclusion. Clearly he already knew of Simon's background as he added "with me your commitment to diversity and inclusion will be well demonstrated."

Although he had not been at the board meeting earlier in the week, Simon had clearly brought him up to date with the strategic direction. He appeared very supportive and enthusiastic, especially about the area of corporate social responsibility. It was clear from his career that his interest was grounded in the law but also saw that as a minimum expectation and believed strongly in a much greater level of accountability and moral responsibility in how business generally conducted its' affairs.

When they talked about the values and ethics James said "The problem is that many company's put ethics under the umbrella of the legal team and honestly, even as a lawyer, I have a problem with that. Unless you have the right underlying values, organizations often confuse legal compliance with adequate ethical behaviour. If you have to resort to legal problem resolution, you may already be failing on trust and other values."

"That's an interesting point," Steve replied, "although legal rules and ethical compliance are in a way partners in governance."

"Agreed," James responded, "but ethical compliance is much more about understanding your stakeholder expectations and what society expects in terms of corporate behaviour. Many leaders don't yet realize how much these expectations have been changing, especially with the five generations we have in the workforce now. It's got really complex, and you need to know what these younger generations are thinking."

Steve was glad to hear this, and James' approach to business seemed to complement Steve's ideas. James didn't let Steve off the hook though and asked a lot of challenging , probing questions about how Steve expected to embed these expectations internally within the organization. James clearly saw organizational culture as a core strategic issue. He understood the financial implications of making investments in these areas which were totally invisible using traditional financial reporting. He made some valuable suggestions on how metrics could be developed to better understand these issues.

The meeting came to an end, and James told both Simon and Steve that after the discussion he was even more enthusiastic about being part of the board. While Steve didn't comment, as he would have to provide his input to Simon after the meeting, he did tell James how much he enjoyed the talk and even suggested that he was somewhat of a "kindred spirit" it appeared.

Some time later, Simon followed up with Steve who confirmed that he saw James as a great candidate and would support him 100% with the board.

Judy came in with the draft memo that had been agreed with the board, announcing their support and commitment.

BOARD OF DIRECTORS
MEMO TO ALL STAFF

Dear Colleague,

Growing a people-centric, responsible business

Alongside you all, we want "our business" to play its part, in resolving some of the problems facing our society and the world. We are all embarking on a significant culture change programme that will enable us to play our part as a responsible business.

As a good corporate citizen, our strategy, with your help, is to be a Responsible Business, giving priority equally to people, planet, and profit. We aim to:

- Treat each other and our other business connections fairly and respectfully.
- Ensure that ethical decision making, is embedded into our DNA, through our Purpose, Business Model and Stakeholder Values.
- Create value for all our stakeholders, by providing good jobs, empowering people, and sustaining a safe work environment.
- Ensure fair and transparent processes of governance including fair pay and equal opportunities for all.
- Encourage and enable people to thrive and lead a balanced life.
- Ensure our jobs have a social purpose which contributes to the wellbeing of the world.

These changes which have already begun, are totally supported morally and financially by the Board,

Signed by the CEO and Members of the Board.

Steve looked through the document and commented "this is really great Judy - a super job." He then signed it off for Judy to send a copy to all directors for their electronic signature, after which she would circulate it to all staff.

Steve had completed his questionnaire for the Saturday meeting and been receiving feedback from the other managers about the questions they were being asked to respond to. The memo about completing the questionnaire that had already gone out, had told each person not to dwell too long on the questions but to respond naturally with what they thought the right choice would be.

Steve had asked about people "gaming the system" by trying to answer the questions with what they thought may give the right answer, but Janet Parvane had told him that there were very sophisticated checks and cross checks, which would flag responses that seemed either inconsistent or inappropriate.

Steve had also asked Holly and Mina to update him on the start of the rollout of the Principles, Business Model and Stakeholder Values. It had been agreed that although the first phase was a functional roll-out, a person from the culture change team would attend all meetings to answer questions and provide feedback. It was clear that there was some level of scepticism which tended to vary by department, as well as length of service and age. Holly had pointed out that some of this was to be expected, as so many change initiatives in the past had been, what she called "flash in the pan" approaches. Holly had described it as a traditional fanfare.

"Announce it, big fanfare, roll it out, it stays topical or flavour of the day for a few months and then dies to be replaced by another program." She added, "people just think, keep your head down, do nothing and this will also pass."

Holly explained that this is why people were now typically sceptical of these initiatives - although there was added credibility because at least this time the employees themselves had been involved in developing the ideas. Holly felt that this was going to be the main benefit of the repeated approaches to reinforcement, during the next implementation phases.

The culture change team had worked with John in marketing, to develop what they referred to as their promotional materials. All three statements had been put on various sized laminated cards and were being given to everybody during the sessions. Poster sized charts were also made up and were being displayed all around the premises. Key tags were made up with the purpose statement. John had developed some graphic artwork for people to use as they wanted, which could be shown as an introductory page to proposals and presentations, or anywhere people considered appropriate for promotion. The goal was to build awareness, that would be reinforced by the follow up stages involving cross functional teams.

Steve knew that the roll-out process would take some time and not to expect fast results, although from various input he was getting it did seem that people were beginning to come up with ideas and work together more effectively. One idea that Steve decided would be important would be to have a regular "town hall" meeting with employees. He had been warned that this might be a good forum for delivering information on their progress but that in many cases, it wasn't an ideal approach to getting employees to ask questions. However, Steve felt that people needed to know how he felt about their progress, and how the business was doing so he asked Judy to work on setting this up, and also remind him at the next leadership team meeting to talk it over with his own team.

Finally, Saturday rolled around. Breakfast had been provided and everybody had arrived on time. Knowing that Sarah was now going to join the board as well as her role in acting as an advisor to Steve, he had suggested to his other team members that she join them on the Saturday meeting. This meant that at the meeting there was Steve, Judy, Sarah, and

Janet (the facilitator), plus Liz, from operations, Charlene, director of technical development and innovation, Tony, the director of finance, Josh, director of sales and John, director of marketing.

Steve started the meeting and introduced Janet, who then provided some background on the assessment called "Spark[viii]." This was followed by a number of exercises that gradually introduced the concept of the various personality qualities. Some of the foundational work related the major groupings based on four colours - referred to as empowering green, commanding red, inspiring yellow and conscientious blue. At this point, Liz responded,

"Oh, now I see. This is the same as all those colours programs that end up putting me in a box called 'my type.' I've been through this before and I have to say I already know who I am and what box I fit into."

Janet replied "great observation Liz, but our approach is a long way away from those programs that focus on types. We believe and evaluate your input, with a belief that you are way more than a type, in fact you are unique. I hope you will see that this is much more than what you may have seen in the past. While we start with the four colours, we then expand this into eight psychological types, twenty four behavioural traits and three, what we refer to as persona. The behavioural traits should be a core point of interest, that will take us way beyond traditional typing. Can we give it a chance?"

Liz was obviously quite sceptical about moving forward. Interesting thought Steve. Liz is great to deal with and a very talented head of operations, but she is also driven to get things done. While she may seem laid back and even passive on the outside, when things needed to get done, you better get out of her way. I wonder what this will reveal about what drives her.

The day progressed with a combination of exercises and referencing the reports. As the process developed the team was starting to realize how accurate the assessments were - both in bringing out personality qualities that they were aware of, as well as challenges that they knew they individually had in some areas. This was increasingly evident as they started looking at the three different persona which (as Janet had explained to Steve) reflected their underlying, everyday, and over-extended or stressed out.

This discussions at this stage became quite intense; the team members had agreed to share their reports with each other, and this generated significant discussion. Some started out defensive as it was revealed that certain behaviours became evident under stress. This brought about an opportunity to have an honest discussion and a developing awareness that "it's OK to be who you are."

The exercise on communications styles was well received when it became clear, because of peoples different qualities and traits, each person liked to give and receive communications in certain ways. As they discussed this they realized that knowing these unique qualities about each other, would allow them to adjust their communication styles with different people.

This would allow more focus on the message and possibly create less frustration, when some people, who didn't like small talk, would eventually say to their colleague - "just get on with it." They did an exercise that helped this where they shared preferred communication styles with each other. The results looked like this:

		COMMUNICATIONS PREFERENCES SUMMARY
Great Toys Ltd	**Team name**	Corporate leadership team
	Date	May XXXX

Name	When communicating with me, I like you to...	When communicating with me, I don't like it when you...	What I offer our high performing team
Liz McIntyre	Be fully aware of the current situation and have evidence to back up their point. Be positive and direct to the point.	Ask to explain my ideas focused too much on only the theoretical side of things.	I have a reputation for doing whatever is needed to get the job done.
Charlene Johnstone	Present arguments rationally in an environment where this is fostered by empathetic leadership. Whole group contributes and works amicably.	People expect me to accept their views without evidence or analysis. Are quiet and introverted in a group discussion.	Involve all members in team strategy and decision making. Creativity, detail, and accuracy when brainstorming. Initiative to be a team leader.
Steve Eccles	Show that they are reliable by keeping their commitments. Do what they say they are going to do. Express your feelings and beliefs, especially if they differ from my views. Challenge the status quo.	Do not come to the point and beat around the bush. Take the path of least resistance. Hold back your expressions. Hold back the details.	The drive to do what is needed to get the desired outcome. Process focused and time bound. Actions focused on core values. Out of the box creativity – challenging, stretch objectives.
Tony Jones	Support your arguments rationally.	People keep their thoughts to themselves.	Ability to handle complexity. Clarity of reasoning.

All members of the team had selected their communications preferences as well as identified, based on their assessment, the value that each brought to the team. Once they shared this there was again a certain amount of "Ah, OK now I see why you get annoyed with me sometimes..."

One of the major outcomes of the day, was that each participant became increasingly aware of the strengths they brought to the team but also the areas that they were "less developed." Participants had also been asked to look at their "strengths" and choose one or two to add to the communications sheet shown above.

While people were initially resistant to these being called "blind spots," each of them eventually realized that what they were seeing was in fact the reality of how others who worked with them everyday, experienced their interactions. As they shared this it really started to help them understand each other, as well as supporting the value of team and group activity.

In their wrap up discussion the team had agreed that knowing this would be a major support in self-development, as well as supporting the value added that comes from having a group of people with different viewpoints. It was extremely helpful that the twenty four behavioural traits that were discussed had a significant correlation to the items included in the stakeholder values. These twenty four items were:

Conceptual	Tough	Cautious	Accommodating
Imaginative	Competitive	Evidence based	Collaborative
Radical	Logical	Practical	Empathetic
Sociable	Purposeful	Observing	Adaptable
Demonstrative	Structured	Measured	Flexible
Takes charge	Reliable	Intimate	Spontaneous

While the words were not the same, understanding the underlying personality would provide some clues into areas where an individual might be a leader or promoter in a particular stakeholder commitment or may be challenged by delivering on certain commitments personally. As an example, if a person had a lower personality "preference" on the quality of "(being) collaborative," that person may need help, support, and encouragement as Great Toys moved towards an inclusionary workplace environment. Steve asked at the end of the day,

"So, you have had the chance to experience this type of understanding and sharing. What do you think about it? Can we use it as part of our supervisory development or other activities? For me personally, I think this ability to 'look in the mirror' at myself as others see me, has been really eye-opening."

Tony naturally wanted people to realize money was involved,

"It seems like a good investment to me. I know what we are paying for this workshop, and what it costs for each person to have their own personal Spark assessment from Collective Minds."

"So, what are we paying" Liz asked, wanting to get to the facts.

When they group was told, they were surprised as the individual assessments were quite inexpensive.

"But remember" Janet added, "that we had what is known as a facilitated discussion here today. That adds to the costs, but you have some choices. One or more people internally could be trained to understand and administer this, then you could have both team sessions like this, plus you could internally provide one-on-one coaching."

"If we could do that" John suggested, "surely we could then use it as an additional check on hiring, as well as for promotions and individual development?"

"But is it like a 'one shot deal'?" Liz asked. "If we make the investment is that it? An assessment, feedback and then done. Do people change? Do we need to do follow up's? I guess what I am asking is whether there is some sort of hidden hook here?"

Several of the team laughed, recognizing that the way Liz responded was clearly aligned with her personal qualities. Liz looked at them initially a bit annoyed, but then she too smiled realizing what was happening.

"No, it's not a hook" Janet responded. "But there are two points here. Firstly, once you have a foundation of knowing about a person, this can form a key part of career development for years to come; yes, people do change a bit as they grow and develop but the foundations remain the same. We are who we are. But the other point is that if you want to, you can also use this approach as a base for looking into other areas - such as leadership development. We have an add-on tool that uses the same base data but looks at how these impact a persons specific leadership styles - but they are all optional."

Steve jumped in again, "Given the importance that the culture change team put on the role of supervisors and others in relationship building and developing a safe workplace, I think - no, not just think, I propose that we start to use this approach on all existing people in management and supervisory roles as part of their development plans. I would also suggest - if Holly agrees that we make it a mandatory part of our evaluation on the short lists for hiring as well as promotions."

"Yes, I agree a hundred percent" Holly replied. "I also think we need the ability to do this internally so I would suggest that at some point, when we have the budget, we have at least two people trained to administer and interpret these assessments."

There was a bit more discussion, but by the end of the day the team agreed to move forward. They also agreed that further coaching workshops would be helpful to move them even further forward in their own development. Steve thanked them all for their time and effort, as well as Sarah and Janet for being part of it. With that everyone headed home.

THOUGHTS AND IDEAS

1. Added diversity at the board level supports and complements the commitment to areas like diversity and inclusion.
2. The memo from the board to all staff shows their commitment but also the link to a responsible business.
3. The focus on leadership development is starting using one of many tools available. TIP – try and standardize the tools being used rather than keep changing. Consistency / common language is an important aspect of culture.
4. Again, a facilitator who has been trained in the tool PLUS has experience working with and helping develop leaders is key.
5. Encourage "constructive dissonance" to extract and deal with issues and build relationships among participants.
6. Communications is a core issue needed for change – using the personality aspects of communication styles brings together the task and the human dimension.
7. The leadership team start to understand that understanding and accepting each others unique personality is critical to building trust and collaborating.

It is important to see these "interventions" not as events that need to happen but as parts of an ongoing journey of development. Individual and group human development is not linear but a constant circle (very like PDCA). Every time on person in a group leaves or another is added the human dynamics will change.

14 Enhancing HR and metrics

After the Saturday meeting Steve had hopped in his car and driven home; this gave him some time to talk with Jenny about the experience on Saturday as well as some time away to relax. Jenny as usual, had asked what he had learned personally about his leadership style and what he had learned from the days workshop.

"By the sound of it, you had all had a great experience but what did you commit to do with the information?" she asked.

Steve replied with some general comments about greater awareness, as well as covering their focus on communications styles. Then Jenny suggested something for when he next talked to the team.

"My thought is that personal development is a combination of knowing and doing. Now you all have this much greater awareness of your own natural capabilities, you need to identify maybe one or two specific things you could work on now, to get better. After all, personal improvement is not an event, it's a journey - step by step."

"That makes sense" Steve replied, "I don't know why we didn't talk about that - although we did agree to work on communications."

"I think maybe you should all choose a couple of things where you think you could improve, and what's more you could look for someone on the team who has more of those qualities are work with that individual as a personal coach. This would help build your team relationships as well as develop each of you?"

"That is a great idea" Steve replied and agreed to talk to the team when he returned to the office. In the past Steve might have just banged off an e-mail to the team, but he was beginning to reflect on the message that behaviour would give the others. Would I expect them to be working and respond on Sunday he asked himself? Steve remembered the term reflective leadership[ix] that he had seen somewhere and after Saturday had started to realize that reflecting on how one's own behaviour impacted others, and what message it delivered was an important aspect of values based leadership.

As the weekend ended and he drove back to Two Rivers he was thinking about the progress that had been made and what was still to be done. Several key initiatives were still in their early stages and had to be implemented, while many changes were already underway and needed to be supported and nurtured. It was a hectic time, and they still had the underlying business to run.

First on the agenda was a follow up with Holly, and she had suggested that they meet in her office area. When Steve arrived, Holly took him into one of their meeting rooms that had a logo on the door that read "PPF Centre." He had to ask -

"It's the 'Putting People First' Centre," Holly explained, "it's the name we have given to the place where the culture change team calls home. They needed a central place to meet, and keep track of our roll out process, and here it is." As she ushered him into the room he was amazed at all the information. There were charts and schedules on the wall showing how the progress was being made in every department. It had plans for the roll-out of the next phases. They also had ideas boards and feedback areas. People had jotted notes and ideas on the board and there was a space next to them for feedback that others had provided.

"We did think about calling it our war room," Holly explained, "but decided that sent the wrong message - you know, winners and losers, a finite term, beginning and end - things that that as well as lots of pain and death." Then she laughed and added, "well based on Mina's experience and the team's I would say there is some pain but no deaths yet anyway."

Steve was stunned and pleased, "this is amazing" he replied.

"And look over here," Holly said as she showed him another message board. "We are all concerned about where we go from here so we have this 'Sustainability Board' where anybody can come and put ideas about how we can make sure that employee engagement and involvement can be continued and embedded in our DNA in the future." Steve noticed that someone had written on the board "Responsible Business Circle" with a number of question marks after it – and thought that was interesting given the earlier discussion with Holly about what the team might evolve into later.

Steve was a bit concerned and asked Holly, "what about using social media? Wouldn't that be helpful so that people could submit thoughts and ideas in real tome from wherever they are?"

"Glad you asked," replied Holly smiling. " We actually worked with Heather (Sarah's daughter who has been providing help to John on social media) and she quickly fixed us up with an online system – a mini Facebook if you like – but it is private and only we can access it. At the moment it is focused on purely employee input but we could expand it as needed."

"Whose room is this?" Steve asked Holly who replied, "it is part of HR, but I agreed that Mina and her team needed a spot to call home, so we decided on turning this space into the centre for her team. The great thing is that while the CCT call it home, we have made it available to anyone that is involved in the roll out. Also, because of the role my HR group must play in working with the team, Mina and I often meet in here to review progress and look at how their input is affecting the work that we are doing on policies and procedures. Like a one stop shop."

"Well, I was going to ask you how things are going," Steve replied, "but I guess I have part of my answer."

"It's going well Steve, but here's the thing. Anytime you or any of the leadership team want an update, its here for you to see. Someone did suggest putting the whole schedule on the computer, but we all agreed this would be cheaper, faster, and more effective for this activity."

"So, if I wanted to know what Mina's team schedule was, who was responsible for each activity and what the actual status would be where would I look?" Steve asked.

"Here," Holly replied, pointing to one of the schedule charts. Sure enough, there were the planned events, the steps required, people involved date planned and date completed. One or two had been late but overall, it was clear their roll-out was on track."

"Let me ask you" Steve added, "who thought this up and developed all the materials?"

"The culture change team" Holly replied. "In a few instances they asked for guidance but overall, they figured out what needed to be done, how to do it and what things to track to keep them on time."

"Kind of proves the intent of our strategy doesn't it?" Holly said, laughing. "People have a lot of talent but it's often not seen because they are not given the chance. Here is a great example of a self-managing team, as they call it."

"This gives me some thoughts for another discussion we need to have about metrics" Steve added. "Seems to me that we might simplify our reporting so that the data people need to manage their work, is created, displayed and used locally where the accountability and responsibility lies."

"Simple reporting is going to be critical" replied Holly. "There are so many different things now being added to the list of metrics that need to be reported it is going crazy. Keep it short and simple - or KISS should be our foundation, coupled with information where its needed."

"I thought KISS meant keep it simple stupid?" asked Steve.

Holly looked at him a bit old fashioned with her head on one side. "And using the word stupid would help and support our values in what way again?" she asked.

"Oh yes, we have to be careful with our words," Steve replied. "OK, I get it. Really good point."

"Not to dwell on it, but it's a great example of how we can talk about these values as well as inclusion and other things, but often the slightest use of the wrong word can have an impact. As leaders we need to try and avoid this, but we also need to expect that we will make a few mistakes. Maybe we need a 'wrong word' jar rather than a swear jar for work?" They both laughed.

"Shall we stay here and talk, or head back to the office?" Steve asked.

"I think the office may be helpful; I know you want to talk about my thoughts and progress on pay, and the problem escalation process as well as share some ideas about getting employee input into our decision making. All my info is back there so let's head back to my office."

Holly first went through her progress on pay scales; she indicated that there was a clear two stage process that she suggested they follow. First would be to clean up what was already in place, but second she had some ideas on a more strategic shift that Steve might want to think about. One of the major shifts Holly was recommending was dropping the idea of minimum wage as a base for temporary and new hires and establishing their starting wages for positions that were traditionally minimum wage as a "minimum living wage." Holly explained:

"If you look at the current national numbers, minimum wage is about ten percent below basic living wage, which is related to the real cost of living - and even that is low in reality" Holly said. "As you may know, the UN Social Development Goals talk about living wage as a minimum, so I believe we should set that as our base. Before you ask I have already worked out the financial impact."

Holly went on to explain, and they agreed that they would make the change effective immediately. Holly also talked about the problems of the temporary and part-time work force, which Steve was aware of, after his discussion with Liz. The pay adjustments would solve most of these problems but there was also the issue of not paying any benefits to these people, as well as zero hour contracts which the company had been increasingly using.

"Firstly, I want to stop zero hour contracts" Steve stated. "While as a business person I see their value, I am concerned that they lack any sort of commitment. We need a contingent workforce because of our seasonal business, but there needs to be a balance between that and fairness. We need to move to an alternative approach - maybe like workforce circles. Full time employees at the centre, then people who are full time but shorter hours in the next circle, then in the next part-timers who are on-call for an as and when needed approach etc. We need to work out exactly how we will do it, but the 'zero hours' approach must go. We must ensure what we do is seen as fair. Maybe we can get some other input?"

"OK, I will work on how we do that" Holly replied. "The other things I have done is to ensure all our pay scales have been linked to market and we pay above the median in all cases. These have been linked to qualifications, experience, tenure, and performance. They are progressive and, if you agree will be made available to the staff in terms of where they are within their ranges and what opportunities they have to grow. I will leave these with you to review, together with this." Holly handed him another sheet that laid out a phased in approach to correcting situations where people were clearly "out of range."

Holly then went on to explain her suggestions on the employee problem escalation process. This was based on two tracks; the first would be a fast track to a panel of the CEO, a board member, and an employee representative, that would deal with areas such as ethical violations. The second would be a progressive track, initially starting with an HR facilitated meeting of the two people involved (assuming they couldn't resolve it between themselves). Next would be a circle of your peers involving the individual and if necessary the other party, plus another manager and another employee. There would then be further steps at increasingly higher levels. This seemed to be a good approach and Steve asked Holly to circulate her ideas to the leadership team, and if there were any issues or problems that couldn't be resolved, then ask Judy to put it on the next leadership agenda.

Before they went on to the last point Steve asked, "doesn't this whole idea of "groups or circles" originally come from ancient civilizations that actually used them as their problem solving approaches?" Holly responded, "yes, great observation. In fact, since the 1990's in Canada[x], certain indigenous groups have been training others on how to set up these approaches as a way of dealing with administration of justice. I don't know a lot about it, but I hear it is quite successful and maybe we should find out some more about it?" Steve agreed and they moved on.

The last subject was the whole issue of ongoing employee engagement, in particular about how employee input was to become a parallel and important part of strategic direction and decision making in the future.

"There are two parts of this that we need to think about" Steve started. "Let me deal with the second part first – so as to speak. I want to implement some type of profit or gain sharing approach so that employees can share in the benefits of success that they help create. This will involve some key aspects of both compensation scales and planning in the future as well as ensuring financial viability. So for that part I want you and Tony to work together and come back to me within three months with a proposal that I can take to the board."

"OK," replied Holly, "I am very happy to hear that, and will get together with Tony, but what was the first part?"

"I need ideas on future involvement and engagement" replied Steve. "I don't think we are ready yet to go to some type of two level governance at the board level, but I want, as a minimum, for employees to see that their input is considered a critical component of our planning."

"Seems to me we need two types of input" replied Holly. "I don't see us starting a complicated and bureaucratic process of dealing with the operational nuts and bolts of planning at the lowest levels."

"Agreed" Steve replied. "My concern is related back to out 'great workplace' commitment and its more about broad based issues that are impacting employee engagement across the board. I think if there are some localized issues then those would also be part of the input we need. If you think about health and safety, we have a health and safety committee that focuses in that area - although I know in many cases it addresses compliance. We need a broadening or extension of that. As an example, should health and safety be addressing bullying, unfairness or other behaviours leading to mental health issues? I don't think that is part of their mandate currently?"

"Here's my suggestion" replied Holly. "Let's get the culture change committee to meet with the health and safety committee we currently have and come up with a plan? To me they are the most informed people, and they should be able to provide us with guidance."

"I like that" Steve replied, "although I start to worry about too many committees. Let's go ahead - can you look after that?" Holly agreed and then Steve added, "part of this may also be to keep the culture change team was evolve its role into a central 'voice of the employee' type of group that is open to confidential input from anywhere in the organization. They would continue to be on the lookout for anything that appears to be happening that is inconsistent with our commitments. I see that someone wrote on the board in the PPF Centre 'responsible business circle?' I think maybe that could be the core of what I might suggest that you start with?"

Holly agreed and Steve added a final comment, "my concern with all of this Holly is we get everything on the right track, but them somehow, maybe as we get even busier things happen that I am not aware of, that need to be fixed but I never hear about it. This is one of the biggest problems that CEO's have – they are often unaware of important issues because no one wants to bring them up. This way we should constantly be on the lookout for problems and issues that may have a negative impact on morale and the culture we want to sustain. I have heard from some of my peers that their greatest problems arise from stuff happening in the business that they never get to hear about." Holly agreed and confirmed she would work on developing some ideas. After a short wrap up discussion, they parted ways.

Steve also wanted to start the discussion on metrics. He knew the team was already busy with operational issues but felt that this was a critical component of their people-centric approach. While they had a good feel for financial numbers , although in most cases these focused on activities and outcomes, there was a limited portfolio of items for other critical areas including the human aspects.

His meetings with Sarah had continued to provide valuable assistance and advice and now she was on the board, she had an added perspective. Steve had talked with her at the last meeting focusing specifically on the metrics aspects and on leadership development. They had talked at some length about her observations from the Saturday team development session with Collective Minds. Sarah had been of a similar opinion to Holly that they should exercise caution in developing more metrics.

"Remember," Sarah had said, "everything that has to be created and reported, adds to your overhead costs. Plus, there is an expectation that people need to look at the results and do something about it. Focus on what's value added to you, and that can affirm progress or drive action."

Sarah had given Steve a whole bunch of information about metrics that were emerging for corporate reporting. Most of these included metrics related to people or as it is being called, human capital. These included ideas from something called the GRI[xi], one of the earliest organizations that had developed reporting for the emerging area of corporate social responsibility (CSR) that had evolved into ESG (Environment, Social and Governance) as that area developed. There was a series of metrics from the World Economic Forum[xii], and from other organizations also focusing on sustainability reporting. Another major source for people metrics that Sarah provided, was ISO 30414 a set of guidelines from the International Standards Organization[xiii]. Sarah pointed out that Steve should also refer to the UN Social Development Goals (SDG's), which it turned out he was already aware of.

Steve had turned all these documents over to Tony and asked him to review them and make some suggestions about how they might move ahead, stressing the concept of the choosing the "critical few." He also asked Tony to think about a "measures hierarchy" where operational, activity level metrics could roll up into enterprise level numbers which could form the basis of the board reviews. He stressed the discussion that he had with the board related to their desire to see a broad based performance report.

THOUGHTS AND IDEAS

1. Note Steve's realization that to put "values into action" requires behavioural change – doing things differently.
2. See that Jenny reinforces the importance of iteration in implementation – teach, do, learn, teach, do, learn etc.
3. Amazing what the culture change team has done? They are not only focusing on their task but are learning many new skills – specially communication and implementation. If they were limited to following instructions, learning would be minimal. Experiential learning is valuable.
4. While "fair" pay systems are important, real change requires strategic shifts – moving from minimum pay to living wage; no longer "saving money" by zero hours (zero commitment).
5. Alternative metrics / reporting is important but use the KISS approach (Keep it Short and Simple).
6. Notice that in parallel to these steps in implementation Steve is now starting to plan ahead to look at change needed once their model is functioning effectively.

Once again we see the ongoing implementation being led by the workforce themselves, plus we see the benefits already coming from "empowerment." The changes in policies are starting and procedures are being aligned with values – but the emphasis here is that Steve and his team are on a journey. Each step and success creating a foundation for the next. "Implementation" never stops because the new approaches are becoming "the way we do things around here."

15 Changing how business operates

One of the operational issues that Steve was still concerned about, was their ability to turn the success of their fast development process that resulted in their new products into a replicable, sustainable capability. He had talked with Charlene about this and asked her to propose a way to move forward. She had left a message that she was ready with some ideas and would like to bring along Liz and John to the meeting.

Liz started by identifying the pro's and con's that had been learned from the previous six months since they started the "crash program" to find some ways to fill the revenue gaps. She identified that the three of them, with input from other members of the leadership team had worked on this together, a key aspect had been how well the cross-functional collaboration had worked, and when things had gone off course, where and why this had happened, and what they had learned to stop it happening again.

"We are trying to achieve a number of goals," Charlene explained. "All of us want to fix the development program and we know resources are tight. We also wanted our approach to move away from the blame game and move towards a focus on learning from what went wrong. For us, the key was 'we got the job done, now how can we do it better.' We also realize that moving forward we must somehow embed the team concept into the process and make it a multi-function parallel process rather than our traditional department by department approach with hand off's and going backward and forward on problem resolution."

"Ah," Steve exclaimed, "you remembered my comments about cycle time?" They all laughed.

"We also wanted to ensure that there was a forum for key relationships," John added. "The role that product development can play in working with suppliers, customers and the community is significant. With this sort of collaboration, we can focus on the 'Partners in Play' initiative that Charlene has talked about. All of this activity moving forward can start to carry this as a core part of our branding."

"That sounds like a solid approach" Steve replied. "So, what is the outcome of your discussions?"

"We need to be able to move fast" Liz responded. "In every situation the whole process must be a sort of rapid development and deployment to minimize the whole cycle time. We remember that you talked about that before. The danger is if we limit the people involved, when we scale up and try and push more volume through the process, we are concerned it would all slow down. So, we are proposing a significant shift in how we organize, that reflects the whole company approach to collaboration."

With that Charlene handed out a single sheet of paper. "We thought that if we could explain it on one piece of paper it would meet our goal of simplicity" she explained.

Essentially what the team had come up with was a horizontal organization structure. The process started with a totally open concept for idea generation, that was open to every single person. This meant that every employee could be responsible for identifying the initial seeds and thoughts that were needed for new products that could grow into ideas. All ideas would flow through a fast track decision making approach headed by Liz, John, and Charlene plus the initiator.

If the idea was considered of practical interest, a simple business plan would be developed by a team of one person from each of operations, marketing, and development, again plus the initiator. The group added that they were working with Tony to develop a simple model where they could "plug in the figures." If the project was considered viable to go to the next stage, there would be a leadership team sign off, where everyone had the opportunity to say yes or no.

"But does that add value" Steve asked? "Are there some people on the team that may not have enough input?"

"You may be right Steve," John responded, "but our opinion is that as a leadership team we should all be in this together. After all, I think we are collectively accountable for the business results. If that is correct, we should understand and share the decisions behind the risk we take. We have to start trusting each other."

"That's not the answer I expected" Steve smiled. "However, I do agree with you. That will be an interesting development approach for our leadership team."

"Yes," Liz added, "and once they sign off, they are agreeing to the plan and to supporting that plan in whatever we they are asked to, in terms of support and resources."

"OK, good" Steve concluded. "So on to execution - how does that work?"

"Once we have the sign off, a specific cross functional team is assigned; the core will be an individual from marketing, operations, and development, but it may include others. As an example, if the idea came from someone in accounting that person would be on the team. If it came from a customer then both the sales person as well as a customers representative would be on the team, and so on."

"What are the risks here" Steve asked. "It seems a bit radical?"

"Maybe," Charlene replied, "but if we are to speed up the process or be agile as they say, keep spending under control, and build relationships among people then we have to change the way we do things. We believe this turns the talk about culture change into reality."

"Yes," John added, "and as I see it, the beauty is that it provides a ton of broader experience for people in the company to develop their knowledge and skills. It will also allow us to move to a more flexible approach to doing the work. People on the teams don't need to be physically here all the time but can be working out of other locations."

"Again," Steve asked, "the risks?"

"Clearly the whole thing could fail miserably" Charlene added, "but we are all committed to making it work. We have developed the processes; we have talked with and engaged the people who will be impacted. We may need some patience if we run into some bumps and problems but again this is the only way we will learn. We talked long and hard about alternatives, but the reality is we cannot go back to the old hierarchical, functionally based model if we want to be competitive."

"That I do agree with" Steve confirmed. "What I need from you all, assuming we announce and implement this approach, is absolute honesty. I cannot personally follow up on every project we agree upon, nor do I want to; but essentially if we implement this, we are giving you the management reins and trusting that it will happen. I promise that if you bring me problems and ideas as to how to fix them I will be with you a hundred percent. But what I do not want, is surprises - that will cause me a problem, and it will also cause you a problem."

The team laughed. They talked some more about the changes and how to roll things out. Steve agreed that Judy would be available to work with the team on any announcements that may be needed. One final request that Steve made was that the team start to think about some core metrics to assess both the intake volumes, quality of ideas, and cycle time for development. This way they could focus on managing the process leading up to product availability and revenue generation rather than purely relying on sales forecasts. It was agreed and the meeting wrapped up.

Another key issue that had to be worked on was the need for someone to head up the IT activities. Steve and Tony had talked about this, and Tony had agreed to develop a position description of the type of person he felt that they needed. They had also added into the discussion the points that John had made about needing someone who was more of a knowledge management expert. Tony had provided a draft for Steve to look at prior to bringing it to the leadership team. If their assessment of the investment required to bring someone like this on board was accurate it was going to be a significant financial commitment.

Tony and Holly had explored the strategic direction of knowledge management as a component of intellectual capital, but they had also looked at the broader issue of a holistic approach that brought together social media that John currently had responsibility for, the website, the internal business systems and to layer across this an ability to extract analytical data and massage this to develop a range of analytics that would help improve the quality and speed of decision making.

Because this position would be an addition to the leadership team it would have to be run past the board. Based on that, Steve remembered that Simon had owned an IT business and would probably be a good person to guide his presentation and hopefully a positive decision. He sent Simon a text asking if he would be available for discussing ideas about their IT plans.

When Simon arrived at the office, he and Steve talked about generalities for a time and then turned to the IT strategy as they currently called it.

Steve had already provided a copy of the work that Holly and Tony had completed to Simon for his review.

"Let me start by telling you that I think these two are pretty well on the money in terms of what they are suggesting," Simon started. "Their thinking about where this job needs to go in the future has been well developed and their assessment of the salary of a good performer in this area is in the range."

"Pity" Steve replied. "Somehow I was hoping that this type of person would come a little less expensive than they are suggesting"

"The challenge is," Simon replied, "that there are not a lot of candidates out there who have a strong, state of the art knowledge of the technology together with a broad business perspective. You really need someone who can think like a business person rather than a "techie' but who knows enough about the technology to be able to develop the big picture about how it can all fit together. Combine that with someone who is practical, down to earth and isn't driven by the latest fads, and you really are looking for the veritable needle in the haystack."

"I can see the challenge because I agree with the scope of the job and your comments on breadth and depth" replied Steve. "Is there anything that Tony and Holly may have left out?"

"There are two additional key issues that you need to think about. Although have touched on them in the report I think they need a bigger discussion. First you need to think technical and processing capacity. Will it be in house software or external? How unique really is the business? Do you want to take on the challenge of planning and managing the technical capabilities that are needed, or is this better done externally? By that I mean using the majority of standard, packaged software? Don't get me wrong - most of the good products out there now, are extremely customizable and already have both operational metrics and analytics capabilities built in."

"Alright - I see that as a key issue," Steve replied. "And the second point?"

"It kind of ties in with the first. When you bring someone in for this function they will need resources. Do you want this person to build a core team of people, or do you want this individual to act like an internal consultant, where you don't 'own' the resources but where he or she works closely with a third party provider?"

"I can see how those two points link together" Steve replied, "but is there something else you are getting at?"

"It's back to the whole strategic direction on partnerships and relationships Steve," Simon continued. "There is no reason not to believe that you can develop effective support and relationships with external third parties, but the core question will be, do the resources that you use have enough of a deep understanding of the Great Toys business to know what they need to ask for? It may sound strange, but the risk is that a third party may assign resources to your account who know little about the toys business and who also support other accounts. If they are not close enough to the business you will need people internally who can work with them, but who know enough about IT and the knowledge and information you may need, to guide the external people."

"That's going to be a hard call" Steve responded. "I trust my existing leadership people to run their functions and know enough about the business to work with the other functions, but I would worry about their ability to move to a higher level of knowledge management."

"Don't sell them short," Simon replied. "I think you have a solid and committed group, although they will need ongoing development because I believe you are already stretching some of them; but maybe they can grow into the role with the right person as your 'head of knowledge management' to guide and support them."

"Clearly this decision will also impact the desires and aspirations of anyone who is a potential candidate" Steve asked. "Some may actually want to build their own 'shop' while others may be totally comfortable with leaving all the operational hassle to someone else."

"Exactly" Simon confirmed. "So, it is important that you decide where you want the business strategy in terms of knowledge management structure to go, before you make a hiring decision."

"But maybe we could look for a candidate with the right skills and see where their bias is?" Steve asked.

"You could" Simon countered, "but I think that might be dangerous. While your whole new people-centric business is shifting to more employee input, the role of the board including yourself is to set basic governance foundations. I strongly believe that how you approach a decision like this is a high level strategic decision that you need board support for. Now, I don't suggest you unilaterally make that decision. Certainly, this should be part of your discussion with your leadership team."

Steve nodded in agreement, and Simon continued, "maybe also get some input from people who manage existing functions directly associated with core external knowledge - such as sales, purchasing and HR. They may all have ideas about what approach might work best. But at the end of the day, I think the role should be clearly defined in terms of your structure before you look for the right person."

"OK, I see that" Steve replied. They talked some more about the role and the timing given the importance of knowledge as they move forward. Simon suggested asking one or two consultants for their strategic advice including maybe some of the existing, major third party 'turnkey' service providers who could put forward the pros and cons of different approaches. Steve agreed he would do some more internal discussions and when they were ready both Steve and Simon would jointly bring the proposal to the board. After discussing some other topics, the meeting ended.

One other key issue that Steve had to think about what the request from the board to develop a code of ethics. Originally Steve's research had shown him that many organizations made their code the centrepiece of their expectations for behaviour. He had decided that their approach of defining a purpose and then supporting this with a business model and a summary of stakeholder values was a better approach. It was more focused and certainly easier to remember.

Steve also felt that many codes of ethics were too long and complicated and, as a result had little impact on people understanding what was expected. He believed this was borne out by the number of large companies who had developed and communicated codes but had then become involved in major scandals[xiv]. But if the board felt guidance was needed, clearly he had to come up with a proposal.

Reviewing the board discussion in his mind, and looking back at their three core statements, Steve concluded that an effective code must link back to these three statements but also provide broad based guidance on what ethical behaviour was in reality. Judy had done some research for him on what other organizations had developed and as he expected many were too long and did not reflect what he had in mind.

One code that did interest him was something developed by an organization called "Ethical Reading[xv]." Their code was reasonably short and general and, although it repeated several items already contained in the Great Toys statements, did provide some effective elaboration on the meanings of the words. Based on this example, Steve developed a first draft of a code for Great Toys, which he would then share with both the culture change team and his leadership team.

The draft he produced had an introduction that read as follows:

Great Toys Code of Ethics

Great Toys, and all its business partners and stakeholders, including employees, are committed to supporting and upholding all statutory and legal obligations within which we operate. But we are committed to a level of behaviour that goes over and above the demands of the law.

We commit to behaviour that is based on the moral codes and expectations of the societies within which we operate. We believe that most people know what is right and wrong, and how society expects them behave as individuals. It is the responsibility of everyone to ensure that Great Toys also embraces and delivers these expectations as a member of society. We have defined many of these expectations in our Company Purpose, our Business Model, and our Stakeholder Values. These statements form the foundations of our code of ethics.

To fully reflect our individual commitment to achieving this expectation we ask each person to read, commit to and abide by the following.

"The following" was a table that Steve had created to supplement the words above. After Steve had looked through the values, both what was already embedded in the final documents, as well as the input from the culture change team, he developed the following table to link the documents.

Steve decided to use the concept of "people, planet and profit" which seemed to work well, was easy to remember and was founded in the history of social responsibility. Steve also knew from his research that people, planet, and profit was an enduring theme, that was also embedded in many of the principles of the growing focus on running a responsible business. He was beginning to think that this would be a great long term focus for Great Toys.

PEOPLE	PLANET	PROFIT
I will play my part, within my sphere of influence, in the company commitment to ensure all staff enjoy their work, are motivated, well trained, physically, and psychologically safe, have equal opportunities, a great life balance and are paid fairly.	I will consider the ethical implications, as well as legal, in all my decisions and work practices, which have an environmental impact.	I will play my part, within my sphere of influence, in meeting commercial targets via an ethical, socially responsible, and environmentally sustainable business strategy.
I will always behave responsibly towards my colleagues, the company, customers, suppliers and the wider society with care, respect, integrity, and compassion.	I will play my part in the company commitment to meet the Company's published environmental targets.	I will play my part in ensuring that sustainability issues are embedded into the governance and decision-making process of the company.
I will not undertake nor ask a colleague to undertake any illegal or unethical behaviour.	I will work with colleagues and other key stakeholders to develop and improve the company's contribution to the environment.	
I will work with my colleagues and other key stakeholders to develop and improve the company's social purpose and to meet the company's social purpose targets.	I will play my part in ensuring the introduction of environmental management, measurement and reporting systems that provides the structures and processes that embed environmental efficiently into the company's culture.	
Name:	**Signed:**	**Date:**

This document would then be signed by all the people involved with Great Toys; it would also be offered to external organizations such as suppliers and customers as a commitment that the company itself was making.

Once the draft was completed he asked Judy to make copies for the leadership team, to be circulated as a draft for discussion. He also asked for copies for the culture change team, but also asked Judy to arrange a time for him to meet with them and present his ideas directly to them.

THOUGHTS AND IDEAS

1. Note that the culture change is now leading to suggestions about how to do operational tasks in a different way.
2. There are still goals to be achieved but the focus is more now on how to cooperate and collaborate more effectively.
3. The employees clearly understand the business imperatives and want to align their work / processes with these needs.
4. Note the shift from waiting for direction to taking ownership and exercising initiative. Steve is still coaching and supporting but now operational leadership is shifting downwards.
5. Notice how their "scope" of partners / participants is including all stakeholders – barriers are coming down.
6. Steve lays out "the golden rule." I trust you and delegate, but I don't want surprises. Involve me when you need me.
7. The IT strategy is a challenge – but see how the board (directors) are now an active participant – providing advice and support.
8. Notice how traditional financial implications (outsourcing IT) are now being weighed against effectiveness criteria.
9. Notice the wording of the Code of Ethics PLUS the linkage to a person by personal commitment to upholding it

Notice that the initial focus on building an effective culture in order to achieve optimum business results is now embracing and overlapping with both acting ethically as well as being a responsible member of society. A responsible business. It all seems to come together in doing the right thing.

16 Progress at all levels

It was now well into the summer and the culture change team had been managing the roll out of the behavioural commitments for several months. In parallel, several changes had been made to the company's HR policies and procedures to bring things more in line with the stated commitments.

Hiring procedures had been modified to include a more in depth focus on understanding the candidates personal qualities and preferences, to ensure enhanced onboarding (orientation) and development needs. Every short list individual was now completing a "Spark" assessment and receiving a feedback interview.

There had originally been a process when hiring people to keep the interviews shorter, but to build assurance and evaluation in by having a three month probationary period which included aspects such as no employee benefits for the first three months. The company had decided this was unfair to those being hired, and that "a commitment was a commitment;" better interviewing was considered to be the company's responsibility to assure themselves that "the right person was getting on the bus." All candidates were shown the code of ethics and asked to read through it and indicate if they had any concerns or issues. They were then informed that they would be asked to sign it if they accepted a position.

A system of mentoring and supporting all new hires was introduced similar to a buddy system approach. Additionally, someone from HR was assigned to every new employee for the first six months to act as a "sounding board" for any issues or problems.

The "on-boarding" or orientation approach had been strengthened and was now customized to the level of employee being hired. It was mandatory that on the first day that a person started in their position, a core orientation development module had to be completed on-line, and the results discussed with the persons "buddy" to ensure there were no misunderstanding or problems. This was the point where the ethics statement was to be signed. This elevated the process of orientation for the relationship aspects of the job to be equivalent to the importance placed on task (such as orientation on critical aspects of safety training is considered for operational employees).

Feedback from phase one of the roll-out had been completed; this had focused on deployment through the traditional functional structure of the business. Each "hierarchy" starting with the direct reports to the leadership team member, communicated the purpose, business model and stakeholder values down through their organization to the most junior people in the organization. There had been significant feedback and number of strategic issues were raised that needed to be addressed.

One of the most important issues raised, was the need to change an apparent bias that a large number of employees felt about the "shareholders are lining their own pockets" and that "this is all words" with many people being sceptical that real change would take place. There were several situations raised where poor treatment of customers, abuse of suppliers by not honouring contractual terms around payments, and cases of harassment of employees by some supervisors, which had been reported back through the culture change team.

When the culture change team brought all the feedback together they shared comments such as:

"Well, we are not treating customers fairly today - let me give you some examples..."

"Whenever I deal with people in department X I feel like I am being treated like a 2nd class citizen..."

"It seems like 'person X' is telling her department not to cooperate in this , that, or the other area..."

"Let me give you an example of what I was told to tell a customer that didn't seem right to me, but I just followed instructions..."

"Every time there is overtime available in our department it seems to be given to a few selected people..."

Additionally, some junior managers had expressed frustration

"I try to be open and honest with my staff, but then senior management comes along and sends us off in a different direction with no warning. I can't build rapport and trust with my employees when even I don't know what going on...."

"I know there are some great ideas about how to make our products safer or even reduce costs but whenever I have raised it, the idea is either shot down or stolen by my manager. I just keep quiet now..."

"There is always a push on, to get the financial statements done and I know in some cases things that haven't been shipped show up in the sales..."

"I know some people routinely pad their travel expenses. Often they do it because they know their manager is doing it and think well, why not me..."

Based on these revelations, a second round of functional rollouts took place, where employees were again asked what the "gaps" were between what they saw in their job and the final version of the values and commitment documents. They were asked to identify one thing that had to be fixed. They were also asked to develop a list of "what does this mean to me in my job" that would both act as guidance within their function and also be incorporated into future training. A final question asked was "what have you learned since you have worked here that, had you known it earlier - say as part of your orientation, it would have made your job easier or more productive?

This last question revealed a significant list of things people had learned "on the job" that were critical to performance, and which should have been included in much earlier training. Knowing this would help get employees "up to speed" faster and reduce the frustration levels caused by not knowing something that was assumed to be "common knowledge." These ideas were rapidly incorporated into orientation and training.

This whole process had extended the time for phase one of the rollout but had yielded some very valuable lessons. The very fact that management had listened to the input and changed their plans, as well as incorporating several of the ideas as "quick wins" into the way things were to be done moving forward, started to win some of the sceptics over, and the climate continued to become increasingly participatory.

Phase two of the roll-out was to be a repeat of the phase one approach but was cross-functional and had involved groups of people from different departments. Once again this process had raised a lot of suggestions and ideas, of which a large proportion related to better understanding between departments and the identification of specific activities where inter-departmental cooperation could be improved. One key conclusion from these meetings was the value of more cross-functional collaboration. There was a desire to develop the "circles" approach for ideas, project management and new initiatives and for developing improved communications.

This idea of circles had already been started during the development of the new products that were launched earlier in the year and were to be the approach in the future for collaborative efforts between Great Toys, customers, suppliers, and other potential idea generators. The initial two teams put in place during the initial new product launches had become the template for developing this activity.

Josh in sales had been particularly supportive of developing the circles for customer focused problem resolution. The combination of multiple contact points, cross functional engagement plus the commitment statements was building a solid foundation for collaborative action. They had also re-instituted the original cross functional problem solving team - now as a circle, that collaborated on issues raised through the call-centre that could be seen as opportunities for improvement. This approach was also already demonstrating enhancements in the practical application of the company commitment to diversity, equity, and inclusion. Janice, who had been one of the recipients of the harassment and passive aggression, was finding that as more people got to know her through the circle approach, so the barriers and relationship problems, including the "passive aggression" began to disappear.

One other major change had been initiated when Holly moved ahead with the DE&I real-world training, which was now based on case studies and real life situations and was being facilitated by Janice. It was clear that people were unaware of how the occasional snide remark or the wrong look or something said off the cuff as "just joking" could all create negative feelings.

Another major enhancement came when Steve had asked both Simon and the new Director James from the board if they would be willing to come and "kick off" these development sessions and talk about their own experiences as both visible and invisible minorities. The fact that board members were actually involved, delivered a solid message about the total organizations commitment to the values that it had established. As one participant had said:

"It is great to see that this is no longer about numbers or quotas or being seen to having minorities as part of the workforce. Your presence here tells us that you really are concerned about embedding broad based inclusive and fair behaviour throughout the organization."

Holly and Mina had arrived to give their regular update to Steve on the progress of the culture change circle as they now were calling it; they were also going to discuss both Steve's efforts on a draft code of ethics and get their thoughts on how to approach both people related metrics and further ideas on the way to get employee input into mainstream strategy and thinking.

First they all talked about the circle updates although Steve had been making regular visits to the "People Centre" to see progress for himself. Both of them felt that solid progress was being made and it was a question of keeping going.

Steve handed out the draft code of ethics that he had created and explained about how the board had requested a code be developed as one of the outcomes of them approving Steve's direction with the other documents. Holly had already seen it when it was sent to the leadership team, but Mina needed a few minutes to read it over.

"Well, its OK" she said "but why do we need it? Is the board saying that those other statements were not enough or that they don't trust the employees if we don't have a signature on something?"

"Great comment – and absolutely not" Steve replied, "in fact the board remains a hundred percent supportive on what we are doing. That was the reason why they were happy to support us by developing that letter to all the employees. Their concern was that we state that we expect ethical behaviour, but they felt we needed to explain this in a bit more of a general statement. As you know in some places it is actually legally required that people sign a document like this." Steve paused then added,

"It is also important to remember that this provides some protection to employees, who can point to the document if they are asked to do something they consider against the code."

"I must admit that I do like the fact that it is very short and to the point." Mina commented, and Holly nodded. "It also introduces the overall thinking about the 'unwritten rules of society' and doing what is morally good' - so those are certainly pluses."

"Do you have any reservations about either the wording or about how we should present it to the employees?" Steve asked them both.

"Not really" Mina replied "although I think it would be a good idea to run it past all our team members before we go further. What about the signature - how will we explain that, and is only the employees you are asking to sign it?"

"Glad you asked about that" Steve responded, "most of the recommended approaches that we looked at externally, ask people to sign the statement as a pledge. The idea is to provide some level of assurance that links back to individual responsibility. Also, I personally have been thinking that it will be an important part of our internal control systems. The more we build trust and delegate authority to people, auditors and regulators often see less management control. If we have this document signed, it shows that even though we have delegated authority, the people who are taking up this responsibility are conscious of it."

"I guess that makes sense," Mina replied. Holly then jumped in,

"But you know Steve, if we also had everyone on the board sign this, it would also show that 'we are all in this together.' The commitment is top to bottom. I would also think that as we develop more external relationships, we could share this document with other who may see its value and want to have their people on any joint team or circle also sign it."

Mina committed to get back to Steve within a few days but expressed the feeling that there would be no problems. She also added that if people did have a problem when it came to individually signing it, that in itself would be a good base for a conversation.

"OK, then if we are done with that," Steve stated, "we had also talked about getting input from the culture change team on future strategy, in particular the need to develop people metrics"

"Yes, we did spend some time on that and also worked with some of the cross functional roll out circles." Mina replied, "we used the opportunity to ask them the question about whether they had any concern this was not going to be a lasting change, and if they did what would they suggest was needed."

"What was the outcome" Steve asked.

"Naturally, as we expected there was some concern. Their first idea about developing more opportunities for cross functional work we have already talked about. The second was really a question that they turned back to management, which was 'what do you need to know to tell you the level of collaboration or engagement is dropping' and how often would you want to track this."

"I think that's exactly the question we are looking to answer," Holly replied, "but I think Steve and I are both looking for some guidance on what would be seen as a positive step and what would be a bureaucratic waste of time?"

They all laughed, and Mina suggested, "the most important thing they felt was a regular, fast, what they called health-check. They also felt that there would always be up's and down's on feedback, but the importance of very regular input was that it would focus more on trends."

"Any ideas?" Steve asked.

"Interestingly yes," Mina replied. "I don't know whether either of you know of something called 'the happiness index?' It's a real-time, on line feedback system that enables the constant collection of employee feelings about their overall work situation."

"Well, I have heard of a more global approach called the world happiness index that measures happiness of citizens in various countries," Steve said.

"I have also heard of something like this but is your suggestion something specific?" Holly asked. "Are you suggesting something like this index approach?"

"Yes," Mina replied. "A number of our employees have friends who work in another local company, and they all seemed to know about this approach because their friends had all talked very positively about it. The provider is a company that is UK based, and called thehappinessindex.com, and they appear to offer some really good, fast feedback as well as being able to quickly zero in on the source of any issues. Of course, the value of the tool will only be seen if it connects to a leadership response, but they suggested at least we take a look at it."

Holly replied, "I don't know a lot about that company, but there are many available out there that offer similar approaches, so we should take a look at some alternatives. We should also talk to the local company those friends of the employees work for and get their opinion. I take your point Mina - we need to look for fast feedback. Surveys may have a role but generally they are not fast enough for taking the pulse. Did the team have any other ideas about metrics?"

"One thing that was suggested, is that you need to track the problem resolution process closely as a method of staying on top of any particular areas that seem to have ongoing issues. They also talked about the importance of tracking outcomes - what they mean by that is almost everybody is aware that the reason we are undertaking this culture change is to enhance performance. They know financial results are expected to improve but want to focus on the drivers. Things like tracking ideas, suggestions, and improvements. One mentioned identifying how much revenue is coming from products that are less than three years old. We also need to track relationships between our people internally as well as externally. Again, the culture team felt that an important outcome would be that we are seen to be a great organization to deal with."

"That is amazing," Steve replied. "These people are thinking like business people!"

"They also talked about the need to obtain feedback from the employees on their feeling about matching words and deeds" Mina added.

"I'm not sure what that means?" Steve questioned.

"What it means is now that we have the established behaviours in place which have been committed to be everyone, there needs to be some type of feedback system that essentially asks, 'how are we doing against what we committed to do,' as defined by the expectations in the values."

Holly interjected, "let me ask you this. As an example, traditionally organizations measured feedback from employees about their supervisors in general terms. Are you suggesting we should customize our questions specifically based on the credibility and consistency of supervisors 'living the values' as they refer to it?"

"That was exactly what they were suggesting" Mina replied. "Plus, they didn't see it as some sort of witch hunt or blame game, but as an opportunity to identify issues that they can then sit and work out."

"I for one have found that input from you and the team extremely helpful," Steve replied. "Holly, can you pull these people metrics ideas together and work with Tony to develop something we might use? I have already given him a lot of ideas from the board, and he is developing an approach for Great Toys. One thing the two of you should consider is the need to get information out quickly and make it as public as possible. This might include workplace reporting of some of the data."

"Happy to" Holly agreed, and after some additional discussions the meeting broke up.

At the next team leadership meeting Steve brought everyone up to date on progress and went round the table so that each person could provide an update about both projects they were leading and operational information. There were no problems with the suggested code of ethics, so Steve would take that forward to the board.

There was a bit of a heated discussion when the issue of budgets came up. Steve had known for some time that some of the team had problems and issues with how he viewed the whole resource allocation process. This had been brought to a head some time ago when Liz had told Steve how frustrated she was when her budget "was taken away from her." As they were soon going to be starting their business plan for the following year, Steve decided to address it head on.

He started by saying, "I think we need to talk about what this group of people around the table is responsible for. Why are you all here? What are you doing as a member of the leadership team?"

There was a bit of a stunned silence as each person looked at each other for guidance. "Well let me start you off" Steve continued. "You all remember from the team session we did, that you all bring unique and different qualities to the table, is that fair?"

There was general agreement round the table. Steve continued, "we also talked a lot about the need to 'know yourself to know each other' - do you remember that?" Again, they all agreed.

"So do you love each other?" Steve asked. Now there really were some surprised looks on their faces. Steve laughed. "Maybe I need to explain what I mean?"

A wave of relief went around the table and people looked a little more relaxed, but clearly were wondering where this was going.

"We have two parallel things that we need to focus on," Steve replied. "We need to work together to achieve our business objectives - remember, we called that our task?" Everybody nodded. "And as we need to work together, we need to also focus on the relationship building piece, right?" Again, there was agreement.

"Whose job is it to run this business," Steve asked. Clearly they all felt this was an easy question to answer, and the consensus was that this was Steve's job. "I don't agree," Steve replied. "Sure, I am the CEO. I am accountable to the board. In some cases, I have to make decisions where there are unresolvable differences of opinion. But in terms of running the business, I see everyone around this table as being responsible for doing that. In fact, I cannot run the business without this team." Steve let that sink in. "What are your feelings about that?" Steve then asked.

There were lots of comments, but it was clear that most of the team continued to feel that Steve was the one accountable and responsible for running the business. He then explained a bit further. "I see myself as the conductor of the orchestra, but I don't make the music. Each section of the orchestra has a key role to play and without everyone involved, playing together, we have no music."

"So, in that case," Holly asked, "do you mean that our role as being responsible for managing our functional area is what you expect from us?"

"Well of course that is part of it" Steve responded. "But in my eyes, when you become part of this team you stop being purely a functional head. That in a way is a secondary role. Each of you becomes a general manager in terms of running this business, while also bringing a particular specialized perspective - be it HR, Finance or whatever."

"I'm not sure whet you are trying to get at here Steve?" Liz questioned. "I thought my role was to contribute to the discussions; then you make the decisions, and we are responsible for executing."

"Well, you see, I don't think that works any more - even if it did in the past" Steve responded. "I believe that when we come together around this table it should be that we are 'as of one.' Everybody has an equal say. Everybody is looking at our whole business model and asking how we can best plan our business, allocate our resources, and respond to changes." There seemed to be general agreement, so Steve continued.

"To do that, we have to believe that when we allocate resources, we collectively still have access to all of them. In real terms maybe what I am saying is that approaches like budgets get us into trouble because they may appear to fix our resource allocation, rather than recognizing that we should be constantly moving things around as the situation changes."

"Well, I'm not sure how that would work," Tony interjected. "As the finance person, the reason we have budgets is for its discipline in planning and control. It makes people accountable."

"But does it?" Steve replied. "What if I said to all of you that there are no budgets - we will just control expenditures from around this table. We will set business goals and I would trust you each to only spend what was required to achieve your desired outputs and outcomes. Could I trust you each to do that?"

"Wow, no budgets[xvi]," Liz commented. "That's an interesting concept. How would that work?"

"Well think about it Liz," Steve replied. "You have cost targets for everything you produce. If we go back to our values, you have committed to responsible stewardship, so would you start spending like a drunken sailor? Oh! Sorry, slip of the tongue, Bad expression. But would I have to worry that as a senior executive you would suddenly become out of control?"

"Well not really, I guess," Liz replied.

Steve continued, "and think about the work you have all been through in the last few months with the projects that Charlene pulled together to get those new products out. Everyone of them had a specific project plan with costs associated with the plan agreed to right Charlene?"

"Yes" she replied, "and we used those plans as our basis for what we controlled against - even though the money wasn't necessarily coming out of our own budgets."

"Yes, but I still have some problems with what you are suggesting," Tony replied - clearly starting to feel uncomfortable with where this was going. "Look at all the fuss Liz made a few weeks ago when we wanted to reallocate resources. She acted like she had some pre-ordained right to spending that money. I felt at the time she was wrong. How would your suggestion work if people like Liz acted like that?"

Liz was clearly offended. "That is pure BS Tony. Just because you have always had something against me. Maybe you don't like women, or are afraid of them holding roles equal to your own?"

That clearly was over the edge. "Of course, I like women" Tony responded, adding, "I am married to one."

It immediately went quiet, and several people lowered their heads.

"Wow" Steve commented, "that was uncalled for. "This was a great example of how quickly relationships can break down. That reference was sexist and unnecessary Tony, and Liz, I'm not sure why this discussion upset you."

"Well clearly Tony has it out for me because I am trying to protect my budget - surely that is responsible stewardship?" Liz suggested.

"Not if we all agree around this table, that we are all accountable for running the business and the resources we have are for our collective use to be applied as we see fit as a group. As circumstances and opportunities change, I want our decision making to be as fast as needed to redeploy resources. And so that we are clear, I mean ALL resources, people included." It fell a bit silent, so Steve continued.

"Look, we are all running a system here people - remember, its our business model. WE are all responsible and accountable. Success comes from our joint efforts. Don't get me wrong when I say I don't care about each of your performances and whether you meet your targets. The acid test for us as a leadership team is that we either ALL make it, or we ALL fail."

It was quiet for a time. Steve jumped back in and suggested that they take a break, and that Liz and Tony should take some time together to resolve their apparent disagreement. "Take all the time you need," Steve told them. Having you two trusting each other and being mutually supportive is of critical importance to our success." With that they took a break.

After a while, Steve saw Tony and Liz come back into the meeting room. "OK, lets get back to it" he said. Once everyone was settled, he turned to Liz and asked, "are you two good now?" Liz replied that all was well, then Steve said

"Although that may have seemed painful, I want to thank you both for a great, unscripted example of the challenge ahead of us. You remember I asked you whether you loved each other? I was not prying or anything, but love is an important word. As human beings we are all different as you saw from when we did 'Spark' assessment and exercises." There was clearly developing realization of where Steve was going with this, so he continued.

"These differences are incredibly valuable to us as a group because it means that each of you may see things quite differently. What risks there are in certain actions. What the pros and cons of certain options are. Your individual opinions will be critical in helping us make better decisions as a group. But your differences will also drive each of you crazy - especially as we now know we can change our behaviour when stressed." The team smiled and there were a few nods of agreement, and chuckles. Steve continued.

"To get us through these times we need to build an underlying appreciation for each other. I call it love because in the same way you may love chocolate or something else, you need to have enough passion for it, to want to be part of the whole team. Only if you have the passion for your place on this team and our _collective success_, will we be able to deliver on the leadership that is expected."

Everyone around the table nodded and several indicated that they "were in."

"We are doing a lot of things to change how we run this business" said Steve. "People out there will be watching us. If we cannot work effectively together and build trusting relationships, we will never be able to expect the people who work for us to be able to do it. I commit to you all, that I do indeed love you as a group. I have developed a passion for working with you all to turn this company around. I can promise you some frustrating and difficult times, but our combined talent will take us where we need to go." All of the team nodded in agreement, so he continued.

"I think we should also continue with the team development work that Janet started with us. I believe the better we can get to know both ourselves and each other, the closer and more committed we will become. Change starts around this table people - not by expecting others to change but by us exhibiting a joint commitment to do things differently."

It was quiet. Everyone seemed exhausted as the session had been somewhat emotional. "What do you think - are we all done for today?" Steve asked. There were no dissenters. "I really appreciate what we have done together today" said Steve. "It's Friday night and I know some of you stop by the pub on the way home. Can I buy you all a drink tonight to celebrate our new beginnings?"

THOUGHTS AND IDEAS

1. Clearly the culture change initiative has momentum with many different areas being changed and improved.
2. Note that as typically happens, the intent of the change is not always achieved. New problems arise as things move forward.
3. Accepting these frustrations and dealing with them as they come up reinforces the desire to close the gaps between intent and reality.
4. Notice how real life experience provided by honest employee feedback is being used as basis for further improvement such as in orientation and training.
5. See the evolution of approaches being used – from "team thinking" to the idea of circles.
6. Notice how Steve is continually developing the understanding between he and his team about behavioural expectations and how this impacts operational decision making.

One critical learning must be that the learning that occurs in each organization is unique to that particular business model and people involved. Certainly, obtain ideas from others (e.g., consultants) but ownership of "the right culture" is organization unique. Trying to short cut culture creation by using other organizations approaches is a key risk.

17 Today and tomorrow

Steve finally felt that all the major transitions that were needed had been identified, although many were still works in progress including his own team. It was now over a year since Steve had come back to run the business and things were clearly changing. There was a buzz of enthusiasm around the business whenever he was out in the various departments and work areas. People were more open and smiled more often. If people had something to say they felt more open to express opinions.

Steve had attended another board meeting which had been a much more pleasant experience. The board had decided, with his agreement that Sarah would be offered the role as Chair of the board. The feeling was that she had been of significant value in helping Steve work his way through the challenges that had faced the business. The board wanted her ongoing advice to be available but with the support of a board that would be operating in a more active and engaged approach.

Another major achievement was that the processes which had been put into place to develop new products both internally, as well as with partners such as customers, suppliers and the rapidly developing community network had been delivering results ahead of expectations. Their final quarterly forecast for the year and their projections for the next eighteen months showed a continually improving picture. Debt was starting to decline, and revenues and profits were growing. Meetings with the bank had started to focus more on how they could lend more money to Great Toys, rather than working in fear of default on the debt.

The ideas for a new portfolio of performance metrics were developing and the board agenda now included an in depth review of all the key aspects of their people strategy. Steve had agreed with the board that there would be some level of trial and error with the metrics as they moved forward. They were all agreed that the goal was to arrive at the critical few areas that had to be routinely assessed and were continually making updates and changes; adding new things and dropping measures that clearly were adding no value.

The leadership team was continuing to develop and clearly trust was an emerging part of this. As people working in the organization began to see trust developing between, and among the senior executives, so they seemed to be more willing to open up and work with their associates in other departments. There was almost no "pointing fingers" when things went wrong, and the approach was focused on a combination of fixing the event and determining what needed to change to avoid it happening again.

The improvements to leadership development all the way from hiring, promotions, training, evaluation, and other aspects had been completely re-vamped and improved. There had been some cases where clearly the incumbents were too far down the "technical specialist" role and not only found it hard to develop the leadership skills required, in many cases they clearly decided that they didn't want to do that. There were several resolutions where the individual would not be able to measure up. Some took early retirement; others changed roles in the company and others decided to take their skills elsewhere and focus on career progression driven by their technical capabilities. But in all cases the process was people centric and focused on fair outcomes.

All this activity had started a re-think about career progression and pay scales. Typically, in the past, a lot of people had gravitated to a management role as that was seen as the way for promotion and more importantly, how to make more money. Compensation scales were adjusted to allow high-performance, critical role technical specialists to be rewarded and compensated without having the need to become a manager.

Steve had been able to persuade the board to allow a company wide bonus scheme to be implemented for the first turn-around year. Everybody would get something, although the amounts were not as large as Steve would have liked, it did at least get the message across that there were rewards for being part of the Great Toys team. However, one strategic area that Steve had started to work with the board on was a permanent "gain sharing" plan.

As a second phase, Steve had raised the possibility of looking at some type of employee share ownership program, although this would obviously be more difficult and a lengthy process. The board had already agreed that based on the family ownership and the challenge of succession planning, developing the possibility of an employee owned business would be a worthwhile and viable alternative.

Steve had continued to have a personal desire to enhance transparency and had kept on with the conversation he had started with Jenny about his own pay. It was clear from much of the public concerns that executive pay, in particular CEO compensation was appearing to get out of hand. At one time the normal or average multiple versus employee pay had been about twenty times. In the past thirty or more years this had ballooned to a ridiculous several hundred times. While many CEO's continued to be paid reasonably, Steve felt that there continued a risk that because people didn't know, they would lump him in with "the bad ones." Steve had finally persuaded the board that the compensation "ranges" for everyone on the board would be made public which included his own (after all this was already the reality in many public organizations).

Coming out of this discussion on transparency, there was another idea that raised its head during a board conversation. Several years ago, an idea called "open book management" had been developed and several case studies had shown that organizations which shared increased financial information with employees, gained in terms of an increasing understanding of the key drivers of business expense and how employees fitted into the bigger picture. In many cases employees often had no idea of the total costs of employment including costs that the company was incurring but which never became part of their pay.

Open book reporting often showed that these numbers were both significant but also that in many cases, the cash flow paid out to people working in the business was the single largest expense. Steve wanted them to share more financial information, but the board was not yet convinced of the idea. Tony had been developing several different approaches as to how this might be achieved - all the time looking for simplicity. In other words, trying to share traditional accounting statements was not seen as the solution.

The board was also looking into another idea that had been raised by Sarah. Her experience with selling her own family business, had demonstrated the problem of understanding an organizations true value. It was now widely known that many businesses were putting significant cash resources into building things like workforce depth and capability, internal relationships, supply chain relationships, customer development and relationships and in the case of Great Toys a very significant investment in building a development pipeline that was critical for new products.

As Sarah pointed out, all this money was being spent but it was never reported as a separate item on the financial statements. Additionally, because accounting approaches did not allow these investments to be treated as capital assets and be added to the financial value of the business from an accounting perspective, relying on the accounting records to assess the value of Great Toys as a business was no longer an option.

Sarah had suggested that the Board should have available a better sense of what the business was worth "as a going concern" from year to year. The value of this would be that if they could arrive at a formula that worked, they could assess Steve's performance on both his financial results but also on his ability to maintain or grow the value of the whole entity. As Sarah also put it "if he screws up and starts making money by cutting corners that starts to deplete some of these intangible investments, we shall pretty soon know about it."

Developing this alternative value reporting was an ongoing project. Tony was involved with Sarah and one of the other directors, and they were also working with external consultants and some academics to find new ways of developing ongoing business value. One key idea that was already being implemented, was an annual assessment of the Great Toys brand value[xvii] which formed a significant part of the investments that the company had been making to improve its' products and services as well as its reputation.

Overall, the new strategic direction seemed to be well on its way. Steve had also been asked to join the board of the local Responsible Business[xviii] group and was extremely interested to gradually discover the parallels between his turn around activity at Great Toys and the principles behind the concept of what made a responsible business. He had also become involved with the local venture capital group; it was felt that this would benefit the community through having access to Steve's business advice.

Great Toys was increasingly seen as a partner with a number of small local start-up's and was now firmly embedded with the first stage of its' "Partners in Play" program with the local college. This had been receiving increasing public attention both via social media and also as a result of the videos that were being added to You Tube that helped parents with developing the role of play in their young children's early years.

Media attention was also increasingly coming from these videos and with the links Great Toys had established with academia. This in turn had made the company more visible and Holly had reported back that there was a growing awareness of the company at recruitment events, which had been started again as the new product pipeline was constantly growing the product base.

Steve and Jenny had taken a long term lease on a house locally and the whole family had moved to Two Rivers over the summer. One of their children was now in university and once the school year started again, their other child returned to the city to spend the weekdays with Jenny at the house and then either one or both of them joined Steve for the weekend. It wasn't perfect but it seemed to be working.

Once the decision had been made that Steve was going to stay on with Great Toys as CEO, he and his partner in their own design business, William Melnyk had come to an agreement on moving forward. William would take over control of the business, but Steve would stay on the board as well as financially involved in a minority position. Steve and Jenny had decided that he needed to demonstrate his own commitment to Great Toys, not only by making his personal investment in the venture capital company but had decided with the board to personally invest in Great Toys. This capital injection was to be instrumental in moving their business plans ahead.

While they had not yet hired their new director of knowledge management, Steve and the team had decided that they did not want to "own" the technology and would rather develop a small core of people internally that would develop as knowledge based experts, working with internal staff to develop ways of collecting, storing, and disseminating information about the toy business. They would also work closely to evaluate the data being collected and publicly available to build an analytics approach that would help them spot trends and identify business opportunities ahead of the market.

One of the crowning glories of the year was Great Toys winning the silver trophy as a member of the toy association. This was prestigious as it was voted on by a variety of people that included the toy council members as well as other people associated with the industry. This was recognition by your peers at the best level.

Steve arranged for a major celebration at a local hotel to share this with all the employees. As he said in his short speech of thanks,

"We could not have done this without the help, support, ideas and personal commitment from everyone of you who are part of the Great Toys universe." He had gone on to ensure that some of the suppliers, customers and other third parties at the event were also singled out for their support and help.

After his speech he was approached by the executive director of the toy association who Steve had continued to work with and now had developed a close friendship with. His words were also added recognition.

"When you and I first spoke more than a year ago, I was really concerned Steve. I think I was not alone in wondering whether Great Toys would ever come back to being as good as it used to be. But you have proved it to us all. If the award had been for the 'most improved' company you would have won it 'hands down.' You should all be very proud."

Steve could not have been happier. It had been a tough haul and in many cases supported by his judgement of what needed to change. While he was now sure they were on the right track there was certainly much more yet to do. But now Great Toys was an organization that Steve felt could face change and challenge ahead of anyone else in the industry.

As an effective "reflective leader," Steve was continually looking ahead and asking, "what could we do better?" He had been working hard to develop this type of thinking, initially with his own leadership team, but pushing it down through the organizations. As he had told people it wasn't change for the sake of change, but a recognition that you can never rest on where you are today. One key initiative that he had talked with the team about and then taken to the board was the concept of becoming a "B Corp[xix]." Organizations can earn this accreditation through meeting and being assessed against a set of criteria. The organization is a not-for-profit that defines its role as

"Make Business a Force for Good: B Lab is the non-profit network transforming the global economy to benefit all people, communities, and the planet. We won't stop until all business is a force for good."

It was the last sentence that had attracted Steve and helped him sell the idea to other people. One of Steve's main concerns was the sustainability of the changes that had been implemented at Great Toys. To retain the B Corp recognition the company would have to provide evidence of the continued existence of the criteria required. Steve felt that this discipline would carry a significant return to them, to ensure that their investment had been worthwhile and that their commitment to the broad base of stakeholders would remain at the core of their business.

Great Toys was now a force to be reckoned with in the industry and Steve was widely recognized as a progressive yet inclusive CEO. His success at Great Toys was being written about in many leading business magazines, and in every report the role of the people who worked as part of the Great Toys eco-system was always front and centre. In terms of the market drive towards ESG, the company had changed its' governance structures and approaches, built social accountability and responsibility as a central strategic pillar, and was ensuring that the "E" was addressed both in terms of the quality and sustainability of its operations, and a commitment to no harm to the natural place that provides the home for us all.

THOUGHTS AND IDEAS

1. Business behaviours are changing. Relationships are improving. The board is evolving. Change is well underway.
2. All these changes are evolving into a different way that Great Toys operates. The market is seeing this and taking note.
3. Underlying policies and procedures, particularly in HR have been redeveloped.
4. Notice a common theme – Steve is often reflecting on how others see what he does and uses this as a barometer of how really committed he is.
5. Again, note that while Steve continues with "current" implementation he also looks ahead – things like "open book" sharing with employees. Employee ownership as a way of enhancing engagement but also addressing family ownership challenges.

As readers may realize there is no "end" to this story. The whole concept of culture change is one that makes continual improvement a "way we do business." Steve has shifted the cultural foundation of the business, but the challenge of strategic and operational management remains. Central to our journey though, is the shift from an autocratic, cost driven culture to a people-centric collaboration and cooperation model. While the foundation upon which the business is built is now quite different, the challenge going forward is to leverage this competitive advantage into leading performance.

Fun Returns to Great Toys

18 The History of Great Toys

Great Toys Limited was founded in the 1920's by a Royal Engineer, Alfred Eccles, who loved children and loved inventing toys. In its early years, the company grew steadily. Alfred's son Jack took over in 1947 and the Company grew rapidly during the 1950's, 60's and 70's and became a major player, during this period, in the toys market for boys 5-12 years age group. During this time, the management consisted of the Eccles and their extended family. The company always used technically advanced machinery and placed great emphasis on safety and quality over all other criteria. Jack was CEO from 1947 until the 1980's when he retired and was succeeded by his eldest son Bob who had worked for his father since he left University.

When Alfred set up the company, he was the principal shareholder; some local businesspeople had also contributed start up equity and these owned about 10% of the company. When Alfred retired, his share of the business went to his son Jack. Over the years Jack split his shareholding so that he and his two sons owned 30% of the business each.

The Great Toys brand achieved cult status particularly amongst the "baby-boomers" generation. However, in the mid 1980's, the company was badly impacted by the "Transformer" revolution and the company's profits were hit. Being a family business, Great Toys were slow to make tough decisions about staffing levels and cut back on new product development. This challenge had created internal conflict between Jack and his son Bob and was a major reason for Jack's decision to retire. Steve Eccles, Bob's younger brother had also joined the business when he left University, although Bob remained the CEO.

As business became more difficult Steve and Bob increasingly disagreed on the course of action, and this, combined with the shortage of cash flow resulted in Steve resigning and moving to a nearby city where he went back to his initial passion of product design. Over the next ten years Steve successfully built his own company with his business partner William. Initially Bob was the design guru while he brought William in, as someone to look after the finance and administration as they grew. William eventually became a business partner with Steve.

Great Toys, with Bob at the helm, continued to produce the same style of toys as it did in the 1950's relying, some believed, on the "baby-boomers", buying the toys for their children. It achieved moderate success during the late 80's and 90's. During this period, most staff were kept on. However, there was limited new hiring principally only to cover mandatory positions and replace retirees. To maintain profits after Jacks retirement, Bob was continually trimming costs, limiting pay increases, putting pressure on suppliers for cost cuts and limiting discounting in the marketplace. The company started outsourcing many activities including the development of low cost, offshore suppliers.

During the early 2000's, the toy market was heavily disrupted again, and Great Toys continued to struggle despite bringing some great new products to the market. It relaunched an updated version of the original toys, but this failed to capture the imagination of the buying public although its 1950 products, if in good condition, were selling for substantial sums of money.

In 2014, Great Toys Limited, grew its range of toys quite dramatically adding several cheaper, externally designed, and manufactured toys, but it failed to regain its pre-eminence of previous decades. During 2014/2015 there were several very public scandals involving cover-ups, alleged workplace bullying and a financial scandal and many redundancies. These years were challenging times for Great Toys! The founder Jack died in 2012 and Bob continued to run the business.

Sadly, Bob's tenure was cut short in 2018 when he disappeared on a scuba-diving holiday in the Mediterranean. His wife reported him missing to the local authorities and some days later his body washed up on a small Greek island. His wife Francis and their two children returned home. After the funeral, the will was read and Bob's share in the business went to his wife. With no clear successor in the business, a new CEO was needed but Francis was unwilling to take on the role.

In September 2019, the company approached Bob's brother Steve Eccles, (who had been and remained an avid Great Toys collector) and was now successful joint owner of a design business in a nearby city. Steve had continued to come back to the local area for family events like Christmas, but these were often strained, and the subject of the family business was usually avoided. When asked, Bob always indicated that times were tough, but they were doing OK. When the call came to take over as CEO of the family business, Steve had spent time checking out things with the family as well as Francis and his own business partner. It had eventually been agreed that Steve should go back and give it a year at which point a permanent decision would be taken.

Book One tells the story of Steve's journey to identify the problems and issues the company faces; book two continue the story and focuses on the activities and initiatives that Steve and his team put in place to turn the company around and set it on a new path to growth and prosperity. In doing so, Steve develops and implements   ideas that are consistent with the emerging model for ***responsible business***. One that focuses earning a profit but does so, while adding value for all its key stakeholders.

Fun Returns to Great Toys

Nick had over 50 years of varied work experience including senior general management and finance roles. From 1989 to 2018 he was active in his own management consulting and professional development company. Currently he still spends time on research and writing, that focuses in the areas of organizational sustainability, human capital, and integrated reporting. Nick has experience working in, and with private family business, public corporations, and governments and NPO's, both in Canada and internationally.

Nick is co-author of "Reflective Leaders and High-Performance Organizations" written in 2012 with Dr. Peter Smyth. Nick also wrote "Governance, Accountability and Sustainable Development" (2005), the "Controllers Handbook" (2008) and since retirement in late 2017 has written a number of additional books related to organizational culture and human aspects of business. Nick lives with his wife at an old 1923 log cabin, west of Ottawa, Ontario that sits close to the Ottawa river. His connection to his birthplace in Wallingford, England remains strong.

Contact Nick at nick@eduvision.ca

Fun Returns to Great Toys

19 Books by the same author

"Variance Analysis for Cost Performance Measurement"
"Governance, Accountability and Sustainable Development: An agenda for the 21st Century"
"The Controllers Handbook" (2nd edition)
"Reflective Leaders & High Performance Organizations" (jointly with Dr. Peter Smyth)
"How Accountants Lost Their Balance"
"Corporate Culture: Combining Values and Purpose"
"The Cost of Poor Culture"
"The Tunnels of Wallingford - Fact or Fiction?"
"Understanding and Reporting Human Capital"
"Toxic Culture"

Fun Returns to Great Toys

20 End notes and follow up

In this section, further emphasis is provided to discussions and issues raised in the story. In many situations either the authors experience or knowledge of what types of support available, have been used.

These suggestions should be used in conjunction with the readers own research and also with the resources section of the website provided by Responsible Business.

---

[i] **Gallup surveys**
Gallup provides a great deal of helpful data on the link between employee engagement and overall business performance. Their annual Q12 Mega-survey is a valuable report to review.

[ii] **Good Governance guidelines**
While there are statutory requirements for companies (as well as additional requirements for public "listed" companies), suggested approaches have been developing since the governance crisis of the 1980's. Nowadays there are many good places to seek guidelines for good board structures such as those published by the UK FRC.
See   https://www.frc.org.uk/directors/corporate-governance-and-stewardship/uk-corporate-governance-code

[iii] **Paul Polman and Unilever**
Paul Polman served as CEO of Unilever for ten years and is a strong believer that businesses can be successful at the same time as achieving a social purpose. Unilever had a long history from its founding of a commitment to social responsibility. When Kraft / Heinz proposed an acquisition of the company it was successfully repelled because of concerns over loss of culture.

See https://imagine.one/paul-polman/

[iv] **7 Steps of Highly Effective Leaders**

Stephen Covey developed this concept as his Ph.D. thesis and went on to great success in applying it to business. He followed up with several other books. Several years later his son also wrote a book "Moving at the speed of Trust" which reinforces many of the people-centric culture based initiatives that Great Toys is implementing.

[v] **Leadership styles**

Different aspects of leadership have been developed by the research of Lumina Learning and build upon the foundation qualities that individuals posses. The Lumina Leadership assessment system identifies leading with vision, leading with drive, leading to deliver and leading through people as a core set of capabilities.

[vi] **Team facilitation**

Collective Minds is a fictional name, based on the work and products of organizations such as The Insights Group (insights) and Lumina Learning. The author was trained as an accredited facilitator for Lumina Learning in both Lumina Spark, the foundational assessment tool, and Lumina Sales, a product aimed at understanding and developing buyer and seller interaction.

[vii] **FRC or Financial Reporting Council**

The UK organization established to regulate auditors, accountants, and actuaries, and set the UK's Corporate Governance and Stewardship Codes. The FRC promotes transparency and integrity in business. Their work is aimed at investors and others who rely on company reports, audit, and high-quality risk management.

https://www.frc.org.uk/

[viii] **Spark and Lumina**

Spark is copyright of Lumina Learning Ltd. Lumina Spark is one of the key foundational, state of the art assessment tools. This tool forms the basis of a whole suite of human development tools and support resources from Lumina Learning. These include Lumina Leader that focuses on qualities that people use to exercise leadership roles. Lumina Learning is a UK organization that operates globally, see the Lumina site

https://luminalearning.com/

[ix] **Reflective Leadership**

There are many different resources about this subject. The author, together with Dr. Peter Smyth wrote a book "Reflective Leaders and High-Performance

Organizations" that provide an overview of their experience in working with leaders and leadership teams over about thirty years in their consulting business.

[x] **Circles for problem solving**

For centuries the administration of discipline and justice has been a community led activity. Many of the principles of how "circles" operate in modern business actually come from these old approaches. For more see:

https://livingjusticepress.org/origins-of-circles/

[xi] **GRI Global Reporting Initiative**

GRI was established in 1997, initially after the public outcry following a major oil spill. The organization remains one of the leaders in sustainability reporting guidance, standards, and metrics.

[xii] **WEF or World Economic Forum**

The World Economic Forum is an international non-governmental and lobbying organisation based in Geneva, Switzerland. It was founded in 1971.

[xiii] **ISO, International Standards Organization**

ISO is the global body for national standards organizations world-wide. ISO has issued a wide range of standards, guidelines, and technical documents since its formation in 1947 in England, although it is now based in Geneva. The document ISO 30414 provides guidelines for internal and external human capital reporting (HCR). The objective is to consider and to make transparent the human capital contribution to the organization in order to support sustainability of the workforce.

[xiv] **Ethical failures**

There have been many examples of organizations who have codes of ethics, some even signed by all employees, where reality has not reflected this intent. Probably the worst example was ENRON in the USA where the code was some sixty pages long and signed by the CEO. Questionable conduct was also seen in organizations like Carillion.

[xv] **Ethical Reading**

According to its web site, Ethical Reading exists to help organisations in Reading and their teams do the right thing by each other, the wider community, and the environment and to thrive in the process. It is all about encouraging people to take a compassionate, respectful, and responsible approach when making decisions at every level from the board room to everyday interactions.

See https://www.ethicalreading.org.uk/

[xvi] **No budgets**

For many years a group initially called the Beyond Budgeting Round Table has existed, with many members moving away from budgets as a control technique. This group is now called the Beyond Budgeting Institute.

https://www.bbrt.co.uk/BBRT/bbrt-membership.html

[xvii] **Brand Value**

While typically not measured or reported as part of financial performance, an organizations brand can often contribute 20% or more of an organizations market value. Consulting firms such as Brand Finance and Interbrand had been providing ways to regularly measure this value for many years. There is now an agreed ISO standard that lays out a consistent approach to calculating brand value. ISO 10668:2010 and ISO 20671:2019.

[xviii] **Responsible Business**

This is a term which is appearing more often as an increasing number of people, including many CEO's, start to look for an improvement in the way that business operates. The main goals are having a social purpose as well as focusing on the broad base of stakeholders involved in value creation. Many of the issues and ideas behind Steve's journey have involved discussions with Jim Bignal who founded a not for profit in the UK for this specific purpose.

See https://www.responsiblebusinessmovement.com/

[xix] **B Corp**

This global movement has emerged as a leader in the drive for business reformation. As their website states: We began in 2006 with the idea that a different kind of economy was not only possible, but necessary — and that business could lead the way towards a new, stakeholder-driven model. B Lab became known for certifying B Corporations, which are companies that meet high standards of social and environmental performance, accountability, and transparency.

See https://bcorporation.uk/ and equivalent sites globally.

Manufactured by Amazon.ca
Bolton, ON

29323747R00131